Creative Uncertainty:

A New Philosophy for a World Out of Balance

By

David Keppel

ISBN: 978-1-7377-359-1-5

Creative Uncertainty:

A New Philosophy for a World out of Balance.

Acknowledgments

My deepest debt is to my parents, Grace and John Keppel. This book began in collaboration with John and remains a joint project. In addition, I would like to thank many friends who encouraged me over the years.

I would like to express my gratitude to mentors who did not live to see the manuscript but who had offered to read it and help with publication: Mary Catherine Bateson, Ilya Prigogine, and Armand Marcel Petitjean. I am inspired by their generosity.

Johanna and Tom Robinson, dear friends of my parents and mine, have been outstandingly generous in their help and encouragement.

My friend Rev. Barbara Carlson mentored me through the writing of the book. We met every fortnight, and she read aloud what I had written in the interval. She gently reminded me of my true priorities and renewed my enthusiasm at a time when I was distracted and blocked. Without Barbara's inspiration and encouragement, this book would not exist.

I would like to thank Leigh Hilbert for his kind permission to use his stunning photograph of lava flow on the cover. See his album "Where Lava Meets Ocean." https://www.leigh-hilbert-photography.com/Moltenlavaphotos/WHERE-LAVA-MEETS-OCEAN/i-bs5qwpz.

If you have reactions or suggestions as you read this book, please get in touch. Write to me at keppel@sbcglobal.net. I hope to hear from you.

1 Father and Son: *A Personal Introduction*

My life – or at least my memory – begins on the afternoon of November 22, 1963, the day of John F. Kennedy's assassination. Our family lived in Rio de Janeiro, where my father was Political Counselor of the U.S. Embassy. My mother was having a tea party for the wives of officers in the Political Section in our apartment on Copacabana, a couple of floors down from the apartment of the President of Brazil. The government had officially moved to Brazilia, but no one in the Brazilian elite or the diplomatic colony was in any hurry to leave life-loving Rio. I was seven years old, and on walking through the schoolyard on my way home that afternoon, I had said to myself "Something terrible is going to happen today."

It had not been a presentiment of Dallas. Instead it reflected rising tension in Brazil and in the U.S. Embassy, where my father, John Keppel, was locked in a debate that, bluntly stated, was about how far the United States should go to overthrow our upstairs neighbor, the leftist President of Brazil, João Goulart. Goulart was no Fidel Castro, much less Che Guevara; at most, he was the potential Brazilian Hugo Chavez of his day. He proposed tax reform that forced foreign multinational corporations to invest in Brazil, not repatriate profits, and he wanted to expropriate the large unproductive estates that characterize so much landholding in Brazil, long one of the world's most unequal countries.

The Kennedy administration split over Goulart. On the one side were liberals associated with Kennedy's Alliance for Progress, the successor to Franklin Roosevelt's Good Neighbor policy. On the other side were Cold Warriors and imperialists. The immediate issue was a planned Latin American trip by Kennedy, a Harvard classmate, though not a close friend, of my father. The trip never took place because of Dallas, but in the background was covert aid – money and weapons – to Goulart's right-wing opponents in the Brazilian elite and military.

Kennedy's murder removed the obstacle to the coup, a liberal Alliance for Progress supporter, Assistant Secretary of State Edwin Martin, whom Lyndon Johnson replaced with the more conservative Thomas Clifton Mann. On March 28, 1964, in a telegram declassified after my father's death, U.S. Ambassador Lincoln Gordon cabled Secretary of State Dean Rusk, Secretary of Defense Robert McNamara, National Security Adviser McGeorge Bundy, C.I.A. Director John McCone, and notorious clandestine operator Col. J. C. King, warning that Goulart could make Brazil another communist China. Ambassador Gordon suggests that clandestine services provide an "unmarked submarine to be off-loaded at night in isolated shore spots" with "delivery of arms of non-US origin, to be made available to Castelo Branco supporters in Sao Paulo" to await the appropriate "trigger incident" for the coup. The military dictatorship lasted twenty years, and Brazil's future President, Dilma Rousseff, since impeached by some of the same rightist political forces, was tortured in the regime's jails.

As Political Counselor in the Embassy, John was a leading exponent of the Cold War view that Goulart was sliding toward communism. As a small boy, I was of course not privy to the details of these debates. Even in later years, he never mentioned the transfer of weapons. But I remember his coming home early with high blood-pressure. I remember on another occasion asking him about the rasping noise from my parents' bedroom and his saying to me, "That is your own mother," who had asthma. I remember the night before our departure, when a dapper gentleman turned up at the door of our apartment with replacement salt-and-pepper suitcases (ours had deteriorated) and then invited us to a late night reception with the Generals at the Presidential palace, an invitation my father declined. The gentleman was Dick Walters, the "Army Attaché," that is, the C.I.A. station chief, who went on to play a part in other Latin American coups, briefly became C.I.A. Director, and met his political end in Watergate. Walters had the motto, "Flattery will get you somewhere" and was as much at home with piano wire as with fluent translation.

John was not one for conversions on the road to Damascus or for self-flagellation. He was self-forgiving — he himself would often say, slightly self-indulgent: unlike his occasionally borderline anorexic son, he liked his Gouda. Unlike penitents who enjoy publicly confessing their sins, John did not like to talk about his role in Brazil, even with me. But Rio was the turning point of his life, leading away from the track to becoming Ambassador to the U.S.S.R. and starting a long path that led to this book, as well as his role in the investigation of the Korean Airlines Flight 007 disaster.

John was an occasional — also a somewhat unfashionable, indeed old fashioned -- poet. One of his poems, written about a day of battle in World War II, begins:

Free now to leave the field,
To wander sandy roads
And stare at vines against the sky.

As these lines suggest, John was by temperament artistic, even dreamy; and it was only events that thrust him into public affairs.

He grew up destined for the family art business. His grandfather Frederick Keppel was a brilliant if not unduly pious Irish protestant of Dutch ancestry, who first landed in Canada as a farmer. But he fell off a bale of hay onto a pitchfork that pierced his lungs, gave up farming and went to New York, where he became the first dealer in etchings and engravings in North America. He cultivated Victorian eccentricity, including keeping a crow on his shoulder during meals, more than kindness. When his elder son declined to follow his father in the art business, instead becoming a foundation executive, Frederick Keppel totally disinherited him. It remained to his younger son – John's father – David Keppel to divide the inheritance. That was no great hardship in the plush years before the crash of 1929, when John was twelve. His teen years came with a sense of doom.

John was a shy child, and he passionately loved his toy sailboat. To his surprise, he turned out to be an able student. As a history of fine arts major at Harvard, he wrote his Senior thesis on Francesco Goya's remarkable series *The Disasters of War*.

He would soon witness them. He was a division commander's aide in the Normandy campaign in World War II. This experience, where many of his friends and comrades were killed, convinced him he could not return to the family art business.

In 1947, he entered the U.S. Foreign Service and began studying Russian. He met Grace in Washington as they were both preparing to go to Moscow, and their courtship took place in walks around the Kremlin.

John brought to diplomacy both his natural tact and an artistic flair for interpretation. He became a Kremlinologist. These were Stalin's last days and the period immediately following – a time when the exact lineup at a parade, or small wording differences between the editorial in *Pravda* (the Party paper) and *Izvestya* (the government paper) were the only clues to great power struggles.

Though he was a young analyst, John helped write some of the decisive cables trying to tell a Washington in the grip of Joseph R. McCarthy's anti-communist hysteria that change in the Soviet Union, while slow, was real.

When John died, we called Sir John Morgan, a retired British diplomat, who had been John's counterpart in the British Embassy. He wrote to Grace:

"I have so many happy memories of our time together. To meet you both, on our first diplomatic posting in Moscow, was an inspiration. John's analytical understanding of the arcane ritual in the immediate post-Stalin era – of what actually went on in the Kremlin – was the envy of all the diplomatic missions. We thought we were pretty good in our own Embassy – but John got it right and we did not."

But John did not get it right in Brazil, and it was the Cold War framework that led him, like so many others, astray. The first lesson he took from the experience was that the United States had no business choosing who should govern other countries or even who was our "friend" there — an obvious lesson, perhaps, but still unlearned by U.S. policymakers. In place of the State Department's traditional area studies and political analysis, John became interested in what he called "functional affairs": food, water, population.

Yet it was not just a new understanding of the dangers of American imperialism that spurred this life-change, but something more personal and painful. John was always torn between the private and public, between lyric poetry and the bureaucratic memorandum. Even when he had been an art student, he was torn: he wanted to draw and paint, but his father asked him to continue the family business and thus to do art history. Only when the war and the State Department displaced that did he have a legitimate reason to tell his father he did not mean to follow in father's and grandfather's footsteps and the firm would thus have to close. Even in his years of great success in the Foreign Service, and even married to my warm and extroverted mother, he was an introvert who held his breath, a habit he said he had acquired listening to a crystal radio set as a boy, and jiggled his knee, to my exasperation for years.

John said that those who get to the top need to have more than analytical brilliance (something he in any case always disavowed): they need the ability calmly to destroy colleagues in bureaucratic infighting. And they need to get out of bed in the morning without the least scruple about their failures, even their crimes against humanity. After the conflict in Rio, the State Department offered him a post in the Embassy in Pakistan, under an Ambassador who was a political appointee, a Coca Cola executive and friend of Lyndon Johnson. John said No and took a more modest job at the Foreign Service Institute, which educates and reeducates diplomats. It was clearly not the route to an ambassadorship. One of my early memories is back from Rio as he explained to a friend why he was doing this. I do not recall the reason he gave at the time.

After a brief time in Washington teaching fellow Foreign Service Officers his old specialty of Soviet politics, he began to reeducate himself. His first step was to take a year's leave to study population at Johns Hopkins, and then, after a couple of years in the population office of the State Department to leave the Foreign Service and work for Philippine politician Rafael Salas in the founding years of the United Nations Population Fund. He relished working in a truly international organization and learning new cultural and intellectual approaches. But he was still restless.

Our family is not alone in this, but we sensed that the global political, social, and ecological crisis at the beginning of a new millennium (after a terrible two decades, one no longer calls it a dawn) is one crisis, and is inseparable from a deep crisis in humans' way of seeing and understanding their world and themselves. It is as basic as the difference between life and machines, or between manipulation and nurture. The manipulative approach is very useful – right up to the point where we can destroy our world and therefore ourselves. At that point – which is now – it is not romantic but simply practical to learn a new way of thinking and acting.

John's eldest sibling, his sister Mary (Dorothy Keppel Fraser) was a microbiologist turned heretic and a key influence. A sickly child, she was a precocious poet but above all a naturalist. Mary became a microbiologist and protégée of Salvador Luria, a Nobel Prize microbiologist at M.I.T. As the Vietnam War put her draft age son at risk, she moved with her son and daughter to Canada, to a part of Vancouver Island that could be reached only by boat, and they built their own houses amid the great trees. By this time, she was a thorough heretic about the genocentric view of life.

In 1974, John retired from the United Nations Population Fund. I had graduated from The Phillips Exeter Academy and entered Winchester College — not a college in the American sense but the oldest and one of the most intellectual English "public" (meaning the opposite) schools. I wanted to go to Oxford and read English literature. Through until my twelfth birthday I was sure I was going to be President when I turned forty, my teen years saw me turn from politics to literature, especially the magnificently complex novels of Henry James, whose writing style I imitated to an exasperating degree.

Given our grossly unequal society's pretense of populism, many writers and almost all politicians would conceal such an experience. But it shaped me in direct ways for which I am grateful and refractory ones that were even more valuable, holding a mirror up to the unspoken snobbery of my upbringing and showing it to be anything but gentle. The British class system, which Americans romanticize watching Masterpiece Theater or, in my case, reading Henry James, turned out — in its "public school" version -- to feature a clever but cruel boy leading others in torturing the fat boy from Yorkshire with asthma and limited money. I wonder whether the victim had a happy life. The tormentor became one of the world's great journalists with a social conscience.

John had been talking about writing a book with the numbing title, "The Crisis of the System." One of the things thirty years of bureaucracy will teach you is to be as bad a writer as possible, so that your official memos are too soporific to be politically damaging. More important, though, was his insight, hardly original but surely central: that we were facing not multiple crises but multiple manifestations of one crisis.

In May, 1975, Grace and John came to see me at Winchester and then we spent the long weekend of a "Leave Out" in the Georgian market town of Blanford Forum. I asked John what he planned to do in retirement. He said that he and Grace planned to write a travel history of New England. With the arrogance of an 18 year-old, I replied, "Oh, Dad, that isn't ambitious enough. Why don't you try to write the equivalent of Montaigne's *Essays* for the present time?" I had been reading Montaigne at Winchester and was fascinated by his digressive style and open mind, so expressive of the possibilities of the Renaissance, liberated from the shackles of the Middle Ages and not yet desiccated by the mechanistic thought of Montaigne's successor René Descartes.

The suggestion intrigued John, and when he and Grace got back to Connecticut, he went to the Yale Co-Op bookstore and browsed for sources. Montaigne, writing at a stand-up desk in the wonderful tower of his small chateau near Bordeaux, wrote his *Essays* as ever more expansive margin notes on the classic texts he was reading. John somehow put his hand on three seminal books that became the basis of our project: Lewis Mumford's *The Myth of the Machine,* Ludwig von Bertalanffy's *General System Theory,* and Hannah Arendt's *The Human Condition.* They opened three great, interrelated questions: What has gone wrong, that humans are now threatening the Earth and therefore themselves? What new ways of thinking are emerging in science, beyond reductionism? How should human society be organized to give people a meaningful life?

The unifying idea here was that whatever was wrong with what we were *doing* in the world somehow mirror an error in our way of *thinking,* and replacing that flawed model with a better one could make a critical difference to the world and ourselves. It seemed obvious but turned out to be a stumbling block with early readers. Surely we didn't imagine that bad philosophy, instead of the military-industrial complex, was the cause of the nuclear arms race? But although ideas do not cause a social system, they tend to mirror it, and new ideas can inspire people to change it.

New ideas are almost never new. Before they are accepted, they seem like recycled old ideas that are not only wrong but irrelevant to the most pressing problems. That is because truly new ideas transform how we see, so when they first appear, it's not clear they have anything to offer to the world, which we still see in the old way. Also, it always takes time to bring the idea into focus and articulate just what it is.

John first wanted to call the book "The Sources of Meaning." He bitterly objected to the commercialism and absurdity of modern life and its celebration of ugliness, embodied for him (perhaps unfairly) in Andy Warhol's presenting Campbell's Soup as art. I wasn't sure where he was going with this, and, as a twenty year-old in academia, was afraid of squishy ideas and sentimentality. John was interested in what he called "the objective basis for ethics," an idea that I had been taught was a beginner's fallacy (following the dictum "You can't derive values from facts").

Thirty years later, I realize John was largely right, though he misunderstood modern art. The source of meaning is life itself — specifically the pattern of living things as contrasted with machines. That is not to say that we are Luddites and want to return to a mythical pure nature. But the organizing principles of life and machines are radically different, and when we live in a world so dominated by machines that they constitute our way not only of thinking but also of acting, then machines cease to be a mere tool and become a prison: instead of just giving us power over the world, they threaten to destroy the world and therefore ourselves.

This threat arises from the different organizing principles of the mechanical and the organic. Machines are designed and built from finished parts; living organisms differentiate, grow, and evolve. This difference makes the most important possible difference: it gives organisms unique flexibility and creativity in a world that is inherently uncertain and unpredictable.

The late 1970s and early 1980s were not friendly years for such ideas. The Counterculture (to which we had been late) was nearing exhaustion and giving way to the market-friendly militarism of Margaret Thatcher and Ronald Reagan. Those challenging these horrors – like his childhood friend and publisher of *The Nation Magazine* Jim Storrow and its Editor, Victor Navasky -- felt they had their hands full and did not need vague philosophy. And we were neophytes, making mistakes that gave anyone with a taste for blood the opportunity to pounce. The first version, by John, was too long and rambling; the second version, largely my work, was too short and dry; the third version did not exist.

The second greatest sin for a writer is to ignore constructive criticism. But the truly unpardonable sin is to let destructive criticism depress you into silence. That sin was mine, and it was an unforgivable betrayal of my ever kind, hopeful, and trusting father, who died without seeing the project brought to fruition.

Whatever happens now, I will always feel my life has been a failure, squandering years of youth and energy when I might have carried a great idea into the world. In miniature, perhaps, but not entirely insignificantly, it mirrors the way my generation squandered its chance to act on global warming, which was clear in my youth; and now we leave future generations an irreversibly damaged world.

Yet taking up the project again, being now my father's age, broken yet whole, perhaps I can speak to a damaged world in a way that neither a retired diplomat nor a clever student was prepared to do. I lost my voice because I did not have my voice; I did not have the voice that I need.

How do you speak when you yourself exemplify much that is worst about the world you want to change? How do you not speak, even, or especially, with the voice that you have? The dated, the archaic, sometimes has in it the seeds of the new. Beyond elitism, beyond privilege, which despite all current intentions will always stain me, I do believe there is in Creative Uncertainty something of immense value and importance that, however undeservingly, we stumbled upon, and which I can use only my own voice to convey. Writing is dialogue in which the written word, even the spoken voice, takes meaning only in the mind of the reader or listener. The writer must submit to be herself, to hope that her embodied self, which you need not like, still offers you someone to identify with – "hypocritical reader, my likeness, my sibling," in the devastating opening to Charles Baudelaire's *Flowers of Evil*.

It remains to say something about the balance of my father's life and a large share of mine. We did not lapse into silence; rather, we took refuge in activism and crisis. Those years, too, were a bitter education.

Those who have seen the film *Bridge of Spies*, about the exchange of Soviet spy Julius Abel for U-2 pilot Francis Gary Powers, will recall the scene in which Mary Donovan (played by Amy Ryan) hears the news the plane is down. It's notable for the huge old radio, the size of a modern oven, and also for the false story in the announcement: that a U.S. weather plane had gone down over the Soviet Union.

In 1960, when this took place, John had been Acting Director of the State Department's Bureau of Intelligence and Research for the Sino-Soviet Bloc, a position he held because his boss had slipped in the bathtub. At any rate, when the U-2 went down, he was part of the working group dominated by C.I.A. Director Allen Dulles, architect of coups from Iran to Guatemala, of the Bay of Pigs, and later, just possibly, of John Kennedy's assassination. The working group did not know that the plane and the pilot had survived: instructions had called for him to destroy the plane on the way down and "spend his dollar" (bite poison). So they had no idea that 24 hours later the Soviets would produce the identifiable wreckage of the plane, including spy camera, and a disgracefully healthy, confessing pilot, Gary Powers. Washington thus put out the "weather plane" story and then, as John used to say, had egg on its face.

On September 1st, 1983, John heard the news that a civilian airliner with 269 people aboard, Korean Airlines Flight 007, had been brutally shot down by the Soviets and everyone had been killed. The flight – the story continued – had gone hundreds of miles off course accidentally, and coincidentally flown right over the Soviet submarine base on Sakhalin Island, off the far eastern coast of Russia and just north of Honshu in the Sea of Japan. In the coming weeks, theories abounded how this could have happened, such as transposing digits in the plane's Inertial Navigational System, with the Korean pilots supposedly too distracted or inebriated to notice. All of this struck John as a new "weather plane" story.

John liked to work collaboratively. He was soon in touch with a Yale graduate student, David E. Pearson, whom he helped write a book on the U.S. Government's cover-up of the full circumstances of the case. At a minimum, it seemed clear that the Soviets had taken the Korean airliner for a spy plane, not deliberately shot down a civilian aircraft full of innocent passengers. So the U.S. government's vehement, almost gleeful denunciations of the Soviets to justify placing new Pershing II and cruise nuclear missiles in Europe, which had faced intense public resistance in Europe, seemed more than a little opportunistic.

One night I answered the phone, and it was Richard Witkin, aviation correspondent of *The New York Times* (and another of John's well placed childhood friends). Mr. Witkin asked John whether he knew the "crazy Frenchman" Michel Brun. John had not heard of him, and Witkin, who never mentioned any of this in his terse reports in *The Times,* gave him his number.

Michel was a professional aviation accident inspector. Small, wiry, a chain smoker, a master in Japanese martial arts, fluent in multiple languages, and owner of a commercial fishing fleet based in Tahiti, Michel was an iconoclast's iconoclast. His trade was proving the official story was nonsense, and whether or not he embraced alternatives for their shock value, shock never deterred him.

What came to be known as the Brun-Keppel Hypothesis was that not only had the Korean airliner flown off course – and deep into Soviet airspace, over its prime nuclear submarine port – intentionally, but it had been accompanied by up to ten U.S. military reconnaissance aircraft. The passenger plane was not so much a spy plane as the provocation of a reconnaissance incident. The big plane put Soviet air defenses in a frenzy, while the other U.S. aircraft monitored the reaction (and learned a great deal that would be useful in penetrating Soviet air defense, should we ever want to launch a nuclear first strike on their submarines in port). Only, something went very wrong, and multiple reconnaissance aircraft were shot down.

Michel had walked up the beaches and picked up debris. Some of it, pieces of honeycomb aluminum that I still have in a storage locker that's my largest monthly expense, may have been from the Korean airliner. He had found them too far to the south in a north-flowing current. (No sign of the plane was ever found in the official search.) Thus, Michel continued, the Korean airliner had not been shot down by the Soviets at all, at least not over the U.S.S.R. Was it hit accidentally by Japanese air defenses in a night sky when all militaries had gone near maximum alert? Or, in the darkest of scenarios, did the "mission's" planners activate an onboard bomb they had placed toward the tail just in case the reconnaissance mission went off track as well as off course?

Did Michel Brun and my father connect too many dots? Or does our jaded distaste for "conspiracy theories" lead us to miss real connections? I do not know. The Soviets famously put their dissidents in psychiatric hospitals. I suspect the case can be told only as a succession of uncertainties, with one clear point: that a series of confusions became the pretext to deploy yet more nuclear weapons and ratchet up the Cold War.

Right or wrong, John became a pariah to his colleagues and even his friends. One of them called to tell him there was a rumor in Washington that he was a KGB agent (a more common rumor regarding Michel, though one John firmly rejected). The story was that he had been recruited as a sleeper back in his Moscow days. There are stories that are meant to be believed. And there are absurd falsehoods whose very absurdity is in your face, a raw display of power. At any rate, John once again put on his pinstripe three piece suit and went to Washington, where

Congressman Lee Hamilton of Indiana, then Chair of the House Intelligence Committee, received him. Congressman Hamilton had notably declined to heed John's previous entreaties to open a Congressional investigation into the KAL case. However, following this meeting, the rumors about my father stopped immediately – something for which I have since had the opportunity to thank him.

Not even bitter lessons ever embittered my father. He spoke with irony of his old trust that his elders and betters were working for the greater good, and that when he found an error, or even a crime, a well written memorandum (somewhat in the style of an embassy cable such as he had written for Ambassador Charles Bohlen in Moscow) would persuade them to correct the error. Even today, that expensive storage locker of mine has not only airplane debris but, in even greater bulk, file boxes of John's letters. No university archive that I have contacted will take them: they want official papers, not the scribblings of one they scorn as a hobbyist. And I will not permit them to be destroyed.

One day, there is a story to be told, perhaps a novel to be written or a film to be made. It would not have to settle which version of the Korean Airline tragedy is correct, but it could tell the story of the split among the next of kin, between those who accepted a handsome financial settlement from the U.S. Government and those, led by a grieving mother who herself had worked in naval intelligence, who refused it. It would tell the story of Michel and John, for what their investigation was and what it might have become. Having gone from conspirator (in the U-2 and in Brazil) to "conspiracy theorist," John knew you could be wrong in both directions. There was also the personal experience of a lifetime of losing the keys to the buildings you had been brought up to own, and no longer trusting what went on inside them.

Rather than being forced into the role of outsider as John was, I began as one. I had not expected to return to live at home after graduating from Oxford, but the summer before my mother told me that "Daddy needs your help." He did. Living at home, I needed a small extracurricular activity, and I became an alternate on the Planning Commission in Essex, Connecticut. Before one of the meetings, the correspondent of the local newspaper, who was my age, invited me to a meeting across the river in Old Lyme of the new Nuclear Weapons Freeze Campaign. My training was in church basements, not in embassies, and it has been a large part of my life ever since.

The Freeze broke with the unstated but firm assumption that you do not make national security policy at a bake sale – and especially that "nice" (spoken with condescension) ladies at a bake sale do not enter its inner sanctum, nuclear policy, whose awesome powers of destruction were the ultimate password of a closed elite. Until the reckless militarists took power with Ronald Reagan in 1981, the crazies had been outsiders or semi-outsiders, like cigar displaying Air Force General Curtis E. LeMay, who had directed the World War II firebombing of Tokyo and would gladly have unleashed full scale nuclear war. He was portrayed with little caricature in *Dr. Strangelove*. No, the center of gravity was somber and devoted to nuclear arms control, an arcane process of bean-counting nuclear weapons on the U.S. and Soviet sides. Meanwhile, technological progress made mere numbers of weapons increasingly irrelevant, and in technology, the United States was in the lead. But that lead was a mixed blessing, because it pushed the vulnerable Soviets, fearful of losing their nuclear deterrent in a U.S. nuclear first strike, toward a posture of nuclear launch on warning, with vast risks of miscalculation in time of crisis.

The Freeze Campaign was built on two innovations, one on policy, the other on politics. The first was that instead of complex bean-counting, the most effective way to cut nuclear danger was a single bold measure: to stop the testing, production, and deployment of new nuclear weapons and of missiles and bombers designed to deliver them. Freezing the qualitative arms race was – and, forty years later, still is – the key to subsequent deep reductions and a world free from nuclear weapons. (Those who naively or cynically said "Why just freeze?" missed that.) The second innovation was to make an international and complex issue a local grassroots issue. The New England town meeting, where the Freeze proposal caught fire, is the closest thing we have to direct democracy, somewhere that every citizen has a voice.

The Connecticut Freeze Campaign was led by inspiring Quakers, the highly focused and charismatic Marta Daniels and the self-effacing Bruce Martin, a labor activist. They introduced me to a world different from the one of officials, even dissenting ones like my father. Empowerment is the antithesis of positional power. The daily work of peace activism is far from glamorous, and, frankly, we have not been successful. Neither has anything else. But how does one measure success? As Beatrice Fihn, a leading activist for nuclear weapons abolition, said in accepting the 2017 Nobel Peace Prize, we face the end of nuclear weapons or the end of us. If there is a history, the failures of earlier peace campaigns will be part of that success.

I long dreaded my father's death for an ignoble reason: as the forever child of loving parents, I feared becoming responsible for the care of my mother, Grace. Yet the six years between John's death and hers were, for me, a belated discovery of a person I had never seen, if only because she had always been there. Deprived of her trademark elegance, removed from her home to a nursing home, denied – by me – the full right to practice her faith (Christian Science, which shuns medicine), and humbled though not humiliated by a gentle vascular dementia, Grace was still, or finally, able to be nothing but herself.

Born in Little Rock, Arkansas, the youngest of three daughters, this beautiful young woman made her way, as a secretary (the only post available to a woman in those years), to the American Embassy in Moscow. In the tight community of Western diplomats in Moscow during the depths of the Cold War, she found a husband (actually had her pick for one) and made lifelong friends, from a homely wire service reporter (Walter Cronkite) to a future British ambassador (John Morgan) to a French dress designer, Germaine Pholabun, who later married a Thai diplomat and settled in Bangkok. In our Connecticut years, Grace became an import agent for Germaine's silks and made another of her closest friends, Bostonian Joan Devin and her daughter Johanna Robinson, who sold Germaine's line (among others) in a boutique in the Ritz Carlton Hotel.

Grace's elegance, even her taste for opulence, misled me as a judgmental young man. I also needed to reject the certainties of the faith in which she had raised me, Christian Science (to which John did not subscribe). Thus it was only in those last years, as I read to her at four o'clock every afternoon – Tolstoy in honor of John, Henry James as an indulgence of my old enthusiasms – that I saw (as everyone around her did) the person I had missed.

My mother rarely frowned; yet she did frown when my father and I talked about Creative Uncertainty. Christian Scientists "know the Truth": they see perfection where the rest of us dwell on imperfection. Yet could "knowing the truth," in a person as warm and outgoing as Grace, be a covert version of "The Wisdom of Not Knowing"?

Grace's standard goodbye was "Drive safely and know that everyone else will too." It sounds strange at first. Obviously she knew that people might not drive safely: otherwise she would not have bothered to raise the subject. But instead of saying "Watch out for crazy drivers" – an attitude that promotes hostility and cynicism – she invited you to see the world with alert optimism.

The world today is not kind to innocent optimism. But it is a time and place in which it is impossible not to be astonished, indeed awed, by the creativity of uncertainty and the bounty of incompleteness. We turn to those patterns for their clues how to repair a broken world and for their pulse of hope when life itself is at risk.

Notes

187. "Telegram From the Ambassador to Brazil (Gordon) to the Department of State." https://history.state.gov/historicaldocuments/frus1964-68v31/d187

"After Lyndon B. Johnson became President in 1963, Mann received a double appointment and was recognized as the U.S. authority on Latin America. In March 1964, Mann outlined a policy of supporting regime change and promoting the economic interests of U.S. businesses. This policy, which moved away from the political centrism of Kennedy's Alliance for Progress, has been called the Mann Doctrine." https://en.wikipedia.org/wiki/ThomHYPERLINK "https://en.wikipedia.org/wiki/Thomas_C._Mann" HYPERLINK "https://en.wikipedia.org/wiki/Thomas_C._Mann"HYPERLINK "https://en.wikipedia.org/wiki/Thomas_C._Mann" as_C._Mann# Brazil

"U.S., Soviets Lied About Plane: Former Official to Dispute Story of Korean Airliner Downing." *The Harvard Crimson* April 29, 1992. "Both the Soviet and the United States governments misled the public about a Korean commercial airliner downed in 1983, a former State Department official will say in a speech at Harvard tonight.

"John Keppel '40, a Foreign Service Officer from 1947-1969, is scheduled to deliver "the Story Behind the Downing of Korean Airlines Flight 007" at 7:30 p.m. in the Starr Auditorium.

"The talk has already caught the attention of local media.

"Keppel said yesterday that he will present the result of his nine-year investigation into the destruction of the aircraft, which killed 269 passengers and crew.

"Keppel's interest was piqued by the improbability of the official positions on the crash of the plane, which was off course over Soviet territory.

"The Soviets said the Korean aircraft flew off course on intelligence purposes, [while] the U.S. said it flew off innocently. However, both governments implied similar things: that the plane was alone when it flew off, that it was alone when it was shot down and that it was shot down off of [Soviet island] Sakhalin," said Keppel, who once served in Moscow." https://www.thecrimson.com/article/1992/4/29/us-soviets-lied-about-plane-pboth/

David E. Pearson, *KAL 007: The Cover-Up.* New York: Summit Books, 1987.

Michel Brun: *Incident at Sakhalin: The True Mission of KAL Flight 007.* New York: Four Walls Eight Windows, 1995.

2 System Error: *A Political Introduction*

A specter is haunting the post-modern world: the specter of uncertainty. A world facing complex existential threats that can only be solved together is torn by divisions that make it seemingly impossible to address even simple problems. Societies so interconnected that they are prey to pandemics are too divided even to agree to wear masks.

Thirty years after the end of the Cold War, the United States and Russia hold ninety percent of the world's nuclear arsenals and base their security on their readiness to commit nuclear omnicide. Nuclear newcomers, and would bes, are considered rogue states, while the global majority demands abolition of these indefensible weapons. Terrorists wage asymmetric warfare, while terrified rich nations darken the world's skies with "Predator" drones hunting terrorists but often killing only the poor. Earth's climate nears the tipping point of catastrophe, while nations and factions cannot agree what sacrifices are needed and who should make them.

Racism and growing economic inequality divide formerly minority majorities and formerly majority minorities into left-wing and right-wing populism. The anxiety of complexity makes certainty more attractive, but fundamentalists who feel no uncertainty themselves are a major factor in global uncertainty. The earlier social contract is plainly bankrupt, fatally flawed and exposed as a tool of oppression. Reforms are painfully obvious; but whether they are sufficient, and whether there is political will to take them, is far from clear. Can we make a more revolutionary change without the traumas of bloody earlier revolutions, which turned utopian dreams into authoritarian nightmares? Do we need collapse, and can we survive it?

Yet uncertainty is more than a threat. It is also the grain of evolution, the law of history, the spark of scientific discovery and artistic creation. It is time to offer its manifesto: a look at creative uncertainty in the natural world and our own lives, a history of the fetish of certainty and its dangers, and a draft program applying the paradigm of creative uncertainty to the problems threatening our survival in the 21st century. Here, in the wellsprings of life and creativity, must lie the basis for a hopeful political program at a time when life on Earth faces an assault of humans' own making.

What is Creative Uncertainty? Start with the CIA model. There is a secret you have to find out. But it might be impossible to find out. We don't know what is currently happening in distant galaxies. We receive only news of their remote past, because information cannot travel faster than light.

But there is another, more radical uncertainty, which is much closer to home. It is not just a limit on our knowing. Instead it reflects the fundamental openness of being. "Two roads diverged in a yellow wood." More than one result is possible. Where "uncertainty of the first kind" is only a limit on your knowledge of a fixed outcome, "uncertainty of the second kind" exists when the outcome is not fixed. It is this uncertainty of the second kind that forms the basis for creative uncertainty; for life, for evolution, for discovery, art, and love.

Although we experience global crisis as uncertainty, that crisis is itself the ultimate result of a misguided, indeed pathological, quest for certainty. This quest has driven much of human history, as a once marginal species sought control over a menacing environment, until we now menace the whole web of life and our own existence.

There are of course many ways of thinking – and still more, of not thinking – but are there not basically two? One is based on the machine, the other upon life. One is closed, the other open. One sees the future as predetermined; the other sees it as creative. One stresses manipulation; the other emphasizes nurture.

All of us use both ways of thinking, often without being aware we have shifted between them. But there is a division of labor. In modern Western culture, mechanism has enjoyed the presumption of "realism." It has dominated the sciences, economics, realpolitik statecraft, and even medicine. The organic view of life has shrunk from a worldview to an ethic of personal relations – when it holds there. It is also natural to the arts – though here too it is under assault.

But the modern division – "businesslike" at work, personal at home – will not hold. If the personal is not political, it risks being commercial: manipulated by images of happiness in the service of profit. On the other hand, every aspect of our common life – beginning with the planet itself – demands our care.

Some may wonder whether a model of thought based upon life is not a bit romantic. If life is part of the physical world, it would seem that it too must obey the deterministic laws which appear to govern the rest. And, in fact, molecular biology and computer science provide powerful mechanistic metaphors of life and mind. If life itself turned out to be a machine, then obviously it could not serve as a contrasting paradigm.

But while biology – a hundred years behind physics – was becoming mechanistic, the deterministic model was melting down at its core, in physics itself. Early in the twentieth century, the Heisenberg Uncertainty Principle set a limit to determinism in quantum physics. Fifty years later, Ilya Prigogine showed that – in the presence of energy – small uncertainties can be greatly amplified and prove decisive at branch points in the familiar world we know. Even more importantly, uncertainty turns out to be more than just a hindrance to mechanistic order. It is the basis of all natural order, from the existence of the universe itself, to the dynamic processes of the Earth (such as weather), through the patterns of life and the creativity of mind.

It is therefore no longer a question of trying to harbor life and save it from the advancing tide of mechanistic, deterministic science. The tables have turned. A life-centered view stressing creative uncertainty is now valid as a cosmology, an understanding that stretches from astrophysics to music. To be sure, this is not a return to ancient metaphors that everything is alive. Life remains a specific, emergent phenomenon in nature. But it is no longer marginal or alien. It is now, in Stuart Kauffman's phrase, "at home in the universe."

In the history of ideas, advances often come from the fusion of two or more ideas already present. If this book – and its central idea of Creative Uncertainty – has something to offer, it is such a fusion.

First, there is the tremendous scientific and philosophical achievement of Ilya Prigogine and Isabelle Stengers. Their work gives physical interpretation and credibility to the insights of philosophers such as Alfred North Whitehead, Martin Heidegger, and Henri Bergson, and stretching back to Heraklitos, that being cannot be abstracted from time. On the contrary, pattern is truly new, unpredictable, and creative. Time – which thinkers such as Plato, Newton, and Einstein held to be a mere illusion – is a stubborn fact. Its flow is irreversible: towards disorder in the stream of entropy, but also (powered by that stream) toward order in the stream of history. If this rich thought can be caught in a single phrase, it is "order through fluctuations": in a sensitive context, normally trivial differences can be amplified to change the course of history, thus giving the whole process its patterned yet unpredictable character.

If these astonishing insights are to contribute wisdom to our global crisis, they will have to enter a dialogue with the ideas of ecology. Ecology helps us understand "the web of life" (Capra): the network of interrelationships that sustain living things. Every organism is an open system in a flow of matter and energy. Every species coevolved with other species that are its environment – while it became part of theirs. Though we have heard these truths for fifty years, they remain anything but obvious. The machinery of "rigorous" thought overlooks them, just as the machinery of "pragmatic" action violates them. The challenge is not merely to pay lip service to ecology, but to rethink everything in its light.

Creative Uncertainty fuses the ideas of novelty with the wisdom of ecology. Neither strand of ideas alone can offer a paradigm for creativity. Uncertainty, like death, is a fact of life; even more basically, it is a fact of the world into which life is born. And just as the denial of death leads to a pathological psyche, the closely related denial of uncertainty leads to pathology – from the quest for an invulnerable missile shield to the attempt to foretell and manipulate life through DNA. But merely accepting death is not enough to make life creative, and the same is true of uncertainty. They demand not only acknowledgement but also creative response. Towards death, we can find this response only in the vitality of our living. For uncertainty, we can find it in ecology, the science of favorable context.

Stripped of an ecological context, Prigogine and Stengers' great insight into "order through fluctuations" can be vacuous if not downright misleading if applied as a social and political paradigm. This is not any fault of theirs but simply a function of extrapolation without development of an idea that originated in a specific context. Prigogine was a physical chemist. He discovered that "far from equilibrium" (that is, in the presence of a flow of energy) systems are both unpredictable and pattern-forming. These characteristics, which we associate so intimately with life, have their roots in the physical world. Naturally, then, he stresses the "far from equilibrium" conditions which incubate this process. But when we cross over to the living world, this idea requires the most careful development and qualification.

"Far from equilibrium" is a qualitative state, not a mere quantity. More in quantity does not always mean more in quality. Living things are "far from equilibrium" in having energy from sunlight or food; but too much food doesn't make them more energetic; it simply makes them fat. Turbulence can stimulate creativity – whether it is an "earthquake" in the ideas of a thinker or a real earthquake that played a catastrophic but creative role in biological evolution. Yet, unchecked, this rhetoric can seem to validate the Austrian economist Joseph Schumpeter's terrible phrase "the gales of creative destruction" – a phrase echoing Karl Marx's celebration of capitalism's revolutionary force and now repeatedly cited by its admirers to legitimate unchecked capitalism's ravages on nature and society.

It is ecology that begins to tell us when – under what circumstances, in what context – the shock of novelty will prove the stimulus to creativity rather than the deathblow to the organism or community. Ecology thus offers the foundation of a science (or art) of nurture. It has direct relevance to the environmental crisis, but also offers a new way of thinking in our social, political and spiritual life.

Yet Creative Uncertainty has as much to offer ecology as ecology offers it. It helps answer a question that has become nagging, even taunting: What is Green, what is natural? Politically, the Green movement tends to split into *Realos* and *Fundis*, to use the German nicknames for realists and fundamentalists. The realists focus on what is "possible" "n Berlin, Brussels, or (worse) Washington. The risk is that in their realism they fail to change the terms of the debate. The Deep Ecologists, or fundamentalists, at their most extreme see humans as a disease afflicting the planet. At its most benign this extremism leads good people to withdraw to small oases of purity; in other cases it can fuel a certainty whose brittleness would betray it in "success" if it did not first lead it into failure.

"Progress," like "change" and novelty," is a term that has been hijacked by technology. There is a tremendous irony here. Obviously industrialism and technology in the modern era changed human society as nothing before had done. The sheer rate of change – and the undeniable rise in living standards for the middle class – made "progress" into a slogan for industrialism. Ever since nineteenth century capitalists used it to dismiss critics of the factory and the poor house, the language of progress has kept its coercive power in debate. It pits "romantics" who "cling to the past" against "realists" who "embrace the future." It imputes the sins of social conservatism to the critics and appropriates reform, even denatured revolution, for the bourgeoisie. It claims to speak for change; it claims this change is good; and it claims that whatever you think of it, you must accept it as inevitable.

The irony here lies in the misleading coupling of machines with novelty, while unmechanized life is presented as archaic. Superficially, it is indisputable: mechanized production displaces hand work; Western culture displaces indigenous culture; industrial human settlement drives other species to extinction. At a deeper level, however, it is exactly wrong to equate machines with novelty and life with stasis. Contrary to science fiction, machines are new only because we as living beings redesign them. It is life, not technology, which is open to unforeseeable change. And while change in some form is inevitable, its specific form is stubbornly and gloriously uncertain.

Novelty is thus the animating principle of living things. It should not be allowed to remain the cudgel with which they are battered. Nor should ecologists, who have grown sick of so called progress, turn against novelty itself. To do so would pit us against the life of life, against the very vitality we are trying to nurture.

It has been said that utopians (and all of us are utopians whether we admit it or not) are divided between those who put their utopia in the future and those who put it in the past. Ecologists are often associated with those who look back to a golden age – and to some extent justly, since humans have destroyed so much of the rest of nature and Western culture has killed off others. But if these tainted conquests destroyed a rich past, they also crushed the seeds of even richer futures. Lost diversity is lost adaptability to unforeseen change. It is no wonder that scientists (and patent-hungry drug companies) are rushing to the rain forest to find the medicinal secrets of vanishing plants and tribal peoples. Tomorrow they will be sold as discoveries. We do not know what might have been the possibilities for cross-fertilization of cultures had the exchange been on more respectful terms.

The true debate is not between "past" and future" but about what future is truly open. Environmentalism is then the struggle to maintain a favorable ambient where unforeseen change can be creative.

I have always felt that thinkers – and their ideas – are at least in part responsible for the ways they are later misunderstood. "Oh that's not what Jesus (or Darwin or Marx) really meant" is no doubt true. And yet I feel the misunderstanding – whether of Christianity, natural selection, or Marxism – must reflect some weakness or one-sidedness in the original formulation. At least, these tragic histories of ideas (which we shall explore further in these pages) should be a warning to those working in the early formulation of an idea. You should worry about this before the conversion of Constantine; and, of course, you should worry about the effect of Constantine's conversion on your movement.

Perhaps the greatest ideas are those capable of self-criticism – because this also makes them open to growth and learning. Here lies the much-publicized secret of the scientific method. In the replicable experiment, it has a way of discarding false theories, if not exactly of proving true ones. Unfortunately, important truths rarely fit the straitjacket of experimental ordeal. They are set aside as unscientific not because they are necessarily false, much less supernatural, but merely because they are complex and unique – and thus cannot be repeatedly tested under isolated conditions.

If Creative Uncertainty is a method, it is a spirit not a formula. What this loses in rigor of verifiable results, it gains in openness to complex problems that make a difference to our lives. Having lived with this paradigm, I think one gets a feel for whether a particular idea or proposal in any field goes with the grain. But it can't and shouldn't be a matter of deductive derivation. We have to be open to new facts and ideas. What we can do is test them for openness. We can look at the pattern for its relevance to patterns in other areas.

This book is an exploration of many fields – from cosmology to biology, from genetics and artificial intelligence to religion, from art to politics – all from a particular perspective. By any other name, this is philosophy. I hesitate to use the word, because philosophy comes encrusted with the scales of centuries of Western thought – most of them, for several hundred years, about the supposed impossibility of a project such as this. Descartes, Berkeley, Hume, Kant, and Wittgenstein all had astonishing insights, but they also deconstructed (i.e. killed) philosophy as a discipline open to all forms of knowledge and unifying of them. Yet they pronounced this death sentence on the evidence of Newtonian science – an objective science where fact could be (and therefore must be) divorced from value. That view of science is now itself obsolete. Philosophy lives.

Philosophy is the art of learning to resist answers that you suddenly realize were buried in the question itself. There could be no better example than two thousand years' insistence on determinism, which was a grim exercise in trying to fit the future into the static terms of grammar and mathematics. But philosophy cannot content itself with criticizing bad theories. It must then open itself to experience – not only scientific and intellectual, but also personal and political, sensuous and spiritual. It must grope its way toward a new view. Henri Bergson was one of the few philosophers with the intuition and flair to do that.

Bergson made some blunders: any open philosophy will. Despite academic faultfinders, an open philosophy will survive its errors. It is not a strict derivation, which would snap with the weakest link in the chain. It is an elastic matrix, in which examples are interpretations. An error on a specific interpretation need not hurt the philosophy, provided its correction strengthens rather than contradicts the broader interpretation in the philosophy.

This book offers a philosophy: a gathering of like-minded interpretations in different fields. It is not a derivation of a new politics from a new science. One reason derivation fails is that every field – very much including science – is itself a human enterprise requiring interpretation. It is thus no wonder that we find raging controversies – with practically opposite views – everywhere we look. The universe of Stephen Hawking is not the universe of Ilya Prigogine or Lee Smolin. The biology of Richard Dawkins is not the biology of Brian Goodwin or Richard Lewontin. The robotic mind favored by Daniel Dennett is hardly the organic one stressed by John Searle and Antonio Damasio. We could wait a hundred years for these controversies to resolve themselves. But we do not have the time. We have to choose.

We have to choose because, while a philosophy of Creative Uncertainty is not a logic-machine "proving" ecological politics, it is an outlook giving us the strength to undertake urgent change.

Uncertainty is not only the specter of possible terrors and disasters. More importantly, it is the condition of hope. Those who refuse it will dismiss the public policies and individual action that offer a possible way out of danger. Consider a planet of seven billion people (eight by mid century), where a few hundred billionaires own more than billions of people combined; where human-caused climate change brings flood and drought, exotic diseases and failed harvests; where other species are dying off as never before; where people are globalized, secularized, commercialized, yet polarized by ethnic background and religious ideology; where the lone and anarchic superpower cannot stop building weapons – which inevitably fall into the hands of outgroups filled with hate. Where, in such a world, is hope?

Even here – perhaps especially here – hope is unaccountably resilient. It comes from the Opposition of Love – a global movement of remarkable unity and diversity. It stands for communities rather than global corporations. It respects nature more than technology. It risks peace instead of war. It has leaders but not authorities. Its activists come from no single background or class: progressive clergy and laity, women, farmers, workers, indigenous people, some intellectuals, but above all simply those – otherwise like their society – who have stepped forward out of personal conviction. The pundits find us easy to dismiss. We are silly like the rest. But this folly is the willingness to look naïve because we refuse to abandon hope.

All efforts to make a better world under these conditions require hope. There are too many logical reasons the attempt "ought" to fail. They can be grouped in the dilemma known as "the tragedy of the commons." This dilemma posits an irreconcilable conflict between self-interest and the common good. And therefore, if some individuals act altruistically for the sake of the community or the environment, others will just take advantage of this to grab more for themselves. The "moral" is that you might as well be selfish yourself – unless someone can devise a system where cheating is impossible. And that is very hard to do. Moreover, we are vulnerable not only to the "rational" selfishness of the relatively rich, but also to the acts of destructiveness of the dispossessed or those who claim to act on their behalf. "Practical," "realistic" people rely on the military and the CIA to protect them from nuclear or biological terrorism. It seems too late to take a risk for peace.

The only answer is that, however compelling, the logic of certainty and security offers only certain catastrophe. Either we survive through some new form of cooperation, or all our lives become miserable and insecure.

These are painfully obvious truths: they hardly require a field trip to explore patterns from cosmology, biology, or art. They may not require it, but I think we do. We cannot guarantee the future we want; we cannot even estimate the probability of its success. In place of these, traditional religion might offer a secure place in the next world. Though easy to mock, this promise at least gave people the courage to transcend their circumstances. Unfortunately, its consolations were too often the opiate of passive withdrawal and its certainties became the text of holy wars. There is no right version of this transcendent certainty. But a translucent uncertainty can help us connect what is creative in nature and ourselves.

In her recent book, *Revolution for Life,* the German philosopher-activist Eva von Redecker says that today's protest movements, including Extinction Rebellion and Black Lives Matter, are fundamentally about life. First, they are defenses of lives, Black, Brown, and indigenous, and in the climate justice movement of life itself. Secondly, in spirit these movements are expressions of life. They are not just Leninist struggles of who-whom, zero-sum games where one group displaces another. Instead they are expressions of our common humanity, which require a more just distribution of income and wealth, and, above all, greater thought for the rights of the unconceived – of the needs of future generations.

The global protest movements are also a "revolution for life" because, like all living things, they embody a principle of creative uncertainty. Uncertainty, we have said, is not a mere limit on our knowing; it is a gateway to creative being, a pattern, or a set of habits, that permits life (far more than machines) to meet unforeseen change creatively. In a period that is marked by anxiety and tragedy, there is also a rediscovery of the world, of its hidden yet manifest patterns, in every facet of life and on all scales. That is a source of wonder, of a new kind of rigor, an of a new kind of political action. We cannot know whether our revolution for life will succeed, but we can feel, right now, that it transforms our ability to see the world in a new way, to feel life more intensely, and to nurture a creative future for those who come after us.

3 The Unpredictable Past

For years, especially under Republican administrations, the United States refused to acknowledge the global treaty banning landmines. Even though the U.S. apparently last exported anti-personnel mines in 1992 and stopped manufacturing them in 1997, the Pentagon deemed them "vital" to our defense and reserved its right to deploy them or transfer them to U.S. allies. There are few images more heartbreaking than that of a farmer or a child in a developing country losing their limbs or life to the buried weapons of a dead war.

History is like landmines: our murderous past has its way of exploding on us – or worse, on those we wish we had never harmed. There is no protected innocence. Though I do not believe in Original Sin (a doctrine invented to put people in the wrong, the better to enslave them), who can escape the unexploded mines of slavery and American racism?

All history is recent history. The universe, which cosmologists tell us is yet young in relation to its lifespan, is thirteen billion years old. Earth is 4.5 billion years old, and life followed in less than half a billion years. Modern humans appeared about 200,000 years ago. But history – which goes with a written record of irreversible events – is just 4,000 years old. Human exploitation of fossil fuels is merely a couple of hundred years old, with more than half the damage occurring since 1980. It's our story, all of it.

In February 2008, the Stratigraphy Commission of the London Society, the oldest and most eminent association of geographers, announced that the Earth had entered a new geological epoch: the Anthropecene. The Commission did not intend this designation as a compliment to Homo Sapiens. It meant that human interventions in Earth's natural systems – notably greenhouse gas emissions causing climate change – had compromised the self-regulation that kept the planet benign to life over the recent period known as the Holocene, in which humans have evolved. We are entering an epoch of unnatural history and, considering the dazzlingly complex balances of nature, it will not be easy to replace nature's services.

There is a paradox in this development. The end of natural history is itself an event in natural history. Human history is ultimately natural history. "All things are artificial," remarked the 17th Century physician-philosopher Sir Thomas Browne, "for nature is the art of God." More familiar to us is the inverse assertion: all things are natural, for even the artificial ones are the creations and extensions of humans, who are part of nature. A bird's nest is not itself a living system; but it is the extension of one; and you can see computers, nuclear weapons, and genetic technologies in the same way. This argument glibly obscures the difference between the organic and the mechanical – and the risk that we become lost in technology's labyrinth.

If you view human history as a chapter in evolutionary history, what a paradox it is! What to the late Victorians seemed a simple story of progress – the triumph of "civilized' races and cultures – looks much more problematic. Twentieth Century anthropology explored the diversity and at times sophistication of non-industrial peoples. Meanwhile it is clear that industrial society may have conquered its rivals but only at the price of environmental damage that makes this society and perhaps human life unsustainable. What a cruel trick natural selection played on us to select us!

It is easy to see how a cactus evolved in a desert ecosystem. It is harder to see how modern industrial civilization evolved in response to any one setting: in fact, it didn't. North America and Northern Europe were home to non-industrial peoples with entirely different relations to the natural world from our own. Nor could "Western civilization" have arisen in the West. It was instead a migratory civilization, like a virus that jumps to a new host before the first dies. This explains the paradox of unnatural history: the development of a civilization that could destroy its environment and therefore itself. It has now reached the scale of the globe. That is why our survival depends on adopting a new way of thinking – of developing a paradigm that works with, not against, nature. But here, let us explore how we got where we are. In the following chapter, we will look at the successes and limits of the mechanistic, deterministic model (the antithesis of creative uncertainty). But conscious thought has been only one influence. There is also history.

In *The Myth of the Machine,* Lewis Mumford sees modern industrialism as a rebirth of the earliest empires. A historian of cities and of technics, and a renaissance generalist, Mumford was deeply disturbed by all-pervasive mechanization. He was not against tools provided they remained to the human scale. But in the ancient civilizations of Egypt and Sumer, he saw a megamachine, a machine made of human parts. These were rigid, authoritarian, warlike societies (even more in Sumer than Egypt) whose monuments show an almost anti–human ideal.

Mumford feared that the megamachine had returned in modern industrial society. Again, the issue is not whether every machine is inherently bad – an absurd proposition. It is that technology becomes so pervasive that the machine becomes a paradigm: the way we see the world and ourselves, the way we structure society, and the way we interact with nature. The clock was the paradigmatic machine: a closed system (except for winding and adjustment) valued for its regularity and predictability. Clocks emerged from the ascetic world of the Benedictine monastery and created a coordinated, mechanical time that was essential to capitalism. The religious "world without women" gave birth to a secular technological culture that is often called materialistic but that is closed rather than open, mechanical rather than organic.

The early 20th Century anthropologist E.E. Evans-Pritchard was bidding farewell at the end of his field work for his celebrated book, *Witchcraft, Oracles, and Magic among the Azande.* His hosts surprised him with a parting question. What oracle was he wearing? Startled, he asked them what they meant. "Why do you always look at your right wrist before making a decision?"

A machine is made out of parts and is assembled; an organism grows and differentiates. The function and use of a machine are determined by the designer and owner; an organism has autonomy and a degree of free will. When the machine goes from being a tool to becoming a paradigm – Mumford's megamachine – both the society and the biosphere are at risk.

In one sense, all things are natural: we and therefore our creations are products of nature. Nature is diverse – diverse to diverse degrees, resilient to diverse degrees. As Evan Eisenberg points out in *The Ecology of Eden,* some of the most disruptive species are not single species but alliances, such as leaf-cutter ants and a partner fungus, that strip the environment through which they eat their way. Humans have in a sense formed an alliance with the crops they eat to plant them instead of the more diverse ecosystem they displace. Forests, perennial shrubs and grasses, other animals, and hunter-gatherer societies have all been the losers. Today even self-reproducing strains of our favorites – corn and soy – are threatened as Monsanto sues independent farmers for patent-infringement.

For vegetarians or vegans, it is ironic that the shift from hunter-gatherer societies to those of settled farmers appears as a fall from grace in humans' relation to nature. How could carnivorous hunters have been gentler than largely grain-eating farmers? Hunter-gatherers were nomadic and did not have time to accumulate possessions that would make them the target of war.

It is not surprising that a conservative, corporate culture has produced scholars who claim – as does Lawrence Keeley in *War Before Civilization: The Myth of the Peaceful Savage* – that early humans were especially warlike and that war in the atomic age has a lower casualty rate. Other anthropologists dispute that. Is Keeley generalizing from the fractured skulls at a few sites? Does he equate family violence or kin feuds with war? Why do such findings produce glee among many reviewers and readers, an inverted naiveté thrilled to demolish any ideal that implicitly makes us look bad? It is not necessary to believe in Rousseau's "Peaceful savage" to distrust the new Hobbesians determined to see non-industrial life as nasty, brutish, and short.

Contrary to any assumption that hunter-gatherers were primitive, these societies show astonishing knowledge of the natural world. Jared Diamond in *Guns, Germs, and Steel,* tells of spending time with New Guinea Highlanders who knew twenty-nine varieties of edible mushrooms and scoffed at him for fearing they might mistakenly take a poisonous one. An archaeological site in the Euphrates Valley in Syria from 10,000 to 9,000 BC shows villagers had collected 157 species. Diamond's chief concern in that book is to explain why agriculture got its first and best start in the Fertile Crescent, giving what became Western civilization a decisive advantage. He traces it to the Mediterranean climate, whose dry summers favored seed-rich annuals suitable for domestication. By contrast, in tropical and temperate forests, plants put most of their energy into wood.

But our question is how agriculture changed our relationship to nature, our way of thinking about the world, and our society. When we plant a crop, we create planned change – and greatly simplify an ecosystem – while resisting unplanned change (such as weeds and bugs). The most striking case is not merely agriculture but alluvial agriculture and large-scale irrigation: Egypt and Sumer, Mumford's ancient megamachine. In a limited area, it was possible to reshape nature, dramatically increase crop yields, and generate a surplus. Michael Mann describes this transformation as "social caging." "The decisive feature of these ecologies and of human reactions to them was the closing of the escape route. Their local inhabitants, unlike those in the rest of the globe, were constrained to accept civilization, stratification, and the state. They were trapped into particular social and territorial relationships, forcing them to intensify these relationships rather than evade them."

Colin Renfrew defines civilization as insulation from nature: "It seems logical to select as criteria the three most powerful insulators, namely ceremonial centers (insulators against the unknown), writing (insulation against time), and the city (the great container, spatially defined, the insulator against the outside)." This caging gave rise to a stratified society. The temple claimed the surplus and redistributed it unequally to an urban elite, including kings claiming divine right – a claim that would, amazingly, survive for millennia.

The city faced raiders and needed raw materials. "War may be endemic," writes Mann, "but centralized military command and conquest are not. They presuppose considerable social organization. It seems plausible that an organizational threshold was passed in Mesopotamia sometime after 3000 BC. The raiding party now had the resources to stay in possession of the enemy's storehouse temple, and stably extract surplus labor services from them. A response was possible: invest in defense"

Empires of domination need ideologies. So to some degree do all societies, of course, but what is striking about these is their claim to certainty. "The emerging institutions of civilization," writes Mumford, "were power-minded, cosmos-centered, mechanically regulated and regimented... By identifying the person of the king with the impersonal, above all implacable, order of the heavens, royal power received an immense supercharge of energy." Mumford notes that the Babylonians eventually "introduced the same concept of predetermined order into the seemingly irregular events of daily life. ...Thus scientific determinism, not less than mechanical regimentation, had their inception in the institution of divine kingship."

How do you tell the story of civilization's violation of creative uncertainty in a way that does not itself violate uncertainty? We know that our civilization is at an impasse. We do not have to prove that everything we were once taught was an advance was in fact nothing but an insidious trap. That would be fundamentalist. There is at least partial truth to the narrative once taught in school: history as progress, not only in technology but also in human freedom.

Compared with the irrigated river valleys of Egypt and Mesopotamia, Greece's "barren hills and extensive rocky coastline" favored decentralized government and trade, not autocracy. Its position jutting into the Mediterranean on the sea route from the Middle East to Europe made it a meeting point of Bronze Age civilization and Iron Age European tribes. Michael Mann thinks the Greek line of battle also contributed to democracy. The phalanx of heavily armed men depended on solidarity; their iron armor was indeed so heavy that running away was not an option. Here Greek men of different classes bonded; it was thus a forge for the *polis,* the Greek political city where citizens could speak and determine their common future. Athenian democracy had its limits: it depended on slavery, and there was inequality among city states. As warfare grew more complex and expensive, the advantage shifted to authoritarian states, culminating in Philip of Macedon's conquest of Greece in 338. What may matter more to us is that while Greece made civilization much more attractive than its Bronze Age predecessors, war and the war against nature remained central to civilization itself. Perhaps this is why Greek thought – notably in Parmenides and Plato – separated permanence from change, a dualism that denies the creative uncertainty of process.

Why do civilizations collapse? Why did the model nevertheless survive?

Rigid, complex societies ultimately collapse as they expand beyond the point of diminishing returns and become vulnerable to shocks they earlier could have withstood. Rome is the most famous case. When Caesar conquered Gaul in 53 BC, Rome acquired great loot in gold. Even the annexation of Egypt (30 BC) was profitable, as Egypt became Rome's granary and it was possible o transport food cheaply by sea. Long distance overland transport was expensive, however, and it was costly to rule the Empire at its extremities, from Albania and Babylon to Spain and Britain. Emperors debased the coin. Undersupplied troops mutinied. "Barbarian" invaders found, in Michael Mann's words, "easy pickings."

Rome's skill at extensive organization – conquest, that is – may have bred indifference to technological innovation. They did not adopt the watermill, which they found in Palestine, or the reaping machine, which was known in Gaul (Mann 284). Some historians note the Romans were accustomed to using slaves and had little interest in labor-saving. Only in the modern world have we discovered that technology can create new forms of mindless work.

Christianity offered inhabitants of a far-flung empire a universal community – something that within Rome's terms had been available only to an elite. Some early Christians may have been radical, but Rome saw a threat even in those who were not, because community outside the channels of Empire seemed itself subversive. By the time of Constantine's conversion in 312, Rome faced a greater threat: barbarians at the gates. Constantine adopted Christianity as an expression of a broader cultural identity in the Roman Empire, one that of course outlived Rome itself. Before Rome expired, the Empire transformed Christianity into a far more hierarchical, even authoritarian creed obsessed with orthodoxy. Its imperial God would profoundly influence deterministic, mechanistic Western science. But that is a story for another chapter.

If civilizations have collapsed so often, how has civilization survived, asks Ronald Wright in his *Short History of Progress*. Part of the answer is that civilization has been like a virus that can infect a new host after the first one sickens or dies. The Fertile Crescent was ideal for the origin of agriculture, because the Mediterranean climate of mild wet winters and hot, dry summers naturally selects annual plants that invest in large seeds. (Diamond 136) By the same token, though, its soil is fragile. Moving agriculture to the irrigated fields of Mesopotamia brought bigger yields and fed larger populations, but the soils succumbed to salinization. Clear cutting and goats stripped Greece's once wooded hillsides. After the collapse of the Roman Empire, Islam took the lead in scholarship and science. Meanwhile, northern Europe became Christian and its deeper, richer soils tolerated and repaid the moldboard plough, raising agricultural productivity and supporting the growth of towns and cities.

Chinese civilization, by contrast, did not have to jump locations to endure. In part this stability was the gift of China's rich ecosystem, but it was also a mark of the caution of its leadership. China, not Europe, first invented printing, gun powder, and the magnetic compass. In the late Middle Ages, its ships traded with India and the Middle East. It was preparing even longer oceanic voyages that might easily have beaten Columbus. In 1433, the Ming Dynasty turned away from ship building to building the Great Wall.

Was China's inward turn xenophobia or a wise refusal to embark on overseas imperialism? Actually Columbus at first met skepticism, even opposition, from Portugal and then from Ferdinand of Spain, who was as obsessed with driving Jews and Muslims from Spain as the Ming were with keeping Mongols out of China. But after conquering Granada in 1492, Ferdinand relented; Columbus was partly funded by private Italian bankers. Were Europe's competing states and emergent capitalists more innovative than the Chinese imperial bureaucracy? That is certainly a version to warm the hearts of free market historians – though Columbus's voyage was more a piece of state capitalism. But irresistible competition is not the same thing as freedom. Without regulation – by consent or by decree – it can be impossible *not* to do something disastrous, because everyone knows that someone else will do it.

North Americans think of land, tobacco, cotton, sugar and slaves, but Spain's genocidal conquest of South America first brought it silver and gold. Precious metals worked a money revolution in Europe. Prices rose; land owners, seeking cash to buy luxury goods, enclosed pastures that had been commons. Desperately poor people from the countryside filled almshouses, workhouses, and urban slums, creating a much larger working class for industrialism. Capitalists and their intellectual allies espoused an ideology of possessive individualism and a supposedly self-regulating market.

For Native Americans, Europeans were first and foremost carriers of germs. In 1930, scholars had thought that only 8.4 million people lived in the Americas in 1491. By 1966, Henry Dobbyns suggested the pre-Columbian Americas had 90-112 million, and that more people lived in the Americas than in Europe. Europeans and their livestock carried smallpox, tuberculosis, anthrax, and trichinosis. Hernando de Soto, who led a Spanish expedition in the Southeast of what is now the U.S., marched with three hundred pigs – his party's meat locker. If only a few escaped and transmitted their diseases to wild animals, those could in turn have wreaked havoc on Indian populations. Evidence is scant, as these populations did not write. But there are two telling points. First, connecting ecosystems that have long been separate often leads to catastrophe. Secondly, if the pre-Columbian Native American population was much higher, then we must revise romantic accounts of the Noble Savage – small bands of hunters – and think instead of densely settled agriculturalists who did change nature but did so in a sustainable way. Indeed, Charles Mann suggests that what early Europeans found was not primitive wilderness but an unnatural wilderness created by the die-off of Native Americans.

The hugely abundant passenger pigeon was an outbreak population filling an ecosystem disrupted by the collapse of the Indian population.

Early English settlers of North America were much struck by the utopian society they found. Were consensus, equality, and respect for nature inherent in Native American society – or were they a paradise built in hell – a humbled society following the epidemics?

But the more significant outbreak population was Europeans themselves, who colonized the Americas and much of the globe. Their breakout was not only extensive – over the surface of the Earth, dominating and sometimes decimating indigenous peoples – but also intensive: through mechanical power and fossil fuels.

For most of human existence, energy was simply human muscle-power, energy drawn from food and ultimately from sunlight. Over history, we domesticated animals – used the ox and horse to draw the plough, the horse, donkey, and camel for transport. We harnessed wind to sail and – a decisive feature of medieval Europe, even of 19th Century New England – the waterwheel for milling and pumping, and for mechanical power. We cut wood for timber, for cooking, and even as a fuel. Steam locomotives in the American West – where wood was plentiful – ran on wood through the 19th Century. But in England the steam engine – first discovered by Hero of Alexandria in 130 BC – was rediscovered by Thomas Savery at the end of the 17th Century and soon improved by Thomas Newcomen to pump water from coal mines. At this point, coal was used for heating: as England recovered from the Black Death and population rose, so did the demand not only for wood but also for arable land. In 1770, James Watt redesigned the steam engine with a governor, permitting it to maintain even speed as steam pressure changed. That made it possible to use steam engines in place of water mills for factory power and, in the 19th Century, for rail and ship locomotives.

With this the demand for coal rose exponentially, bringing the process full circle.

The turn to fossil fuels and power engines thus came from specific practical needs, not from an abstract quest for certainty. The search for certainty had a much greater influence on Newtonian physics, but it was not till the late 19th Century that theoretical science shaped practical invention. However, the spread of machines and huge stocks of fossil fuel to power them does transform the way we see the world – and the way we therefore treat it. When energy is limited to animal power or renewable sources such as wind and water, we are more likely to stay sensitive to the natural world. Consider two roads. One is small and winds its way along the easiest path through the terrain. The other is a superhighway. It blasts through the mountain. Unlimited energy allows us to be hot in winter and cold in summer, to import summer fruit in January – in short, to make the world uniform and predictable. Until it makes it unpredictable in catastrophic ways.

Today an average American has two hundred ghost-slaves. According to David Carpenter in his article "Energy and Evolution," "Today the extrasomatic energy used by people around the world is equal to the world of 280 billion people." It is as if every man, woman, and child around the world had fifty slaves – or, in the U.S. case, two hundred." We may debate whether the planet can support nine billion people, but no one would argue it could support 280 billion. Yet that is our true environmental impact, and it is increasing rapidly as globalization spreads Western lifestyles to the Third World.

It is this impossibility that makes history central to the debate about North-South relations and global warming.

Overseas expansion and technological growth offered the two great escape valves for pressure created in a society that never ceased to be unequal and exploitative. In *Ecological*

Imperialism, Alfred Crosby discusses the conquest and settlement of the temperate Americas, Australia, and New Zealand. Before the American Revolution, half to two-thirds of white settlers were indentured servants, and until 1820 Australia was settled by convicts. In the following century, 50 million free Irish, Britons, Scandanavians, and Southern and Eastern Europeans left for these neo-Europes. They left Europe in order to flee the Irish Potato Famine, the grim conditions of early industrial Britain, and the even greater poverty of southern Italy and Poland.

Industrialization, powered by fossil fuels, displaced handcraft workers such as weavers – thus the Luddites and their French kin, who broke machines. At the same time, it often reduced factory workers to little more than cogs in the assembly line, subject to the inhuman discipline championed by the American engineer Frederick Taylor. If Lewis Mumford's ancient megamachne of Sumer and Egypt had been a machine made out of human parts, the new one was both flesh and steel. Creativity was reserved to the engineer, the God-creator or *deus ex machina* outside the system.

There is no denying that after its wrenching beginnings, the industrial revolution enormously raised the living standard of the working class – in the "advanced' countries," that is. And there's the rub. An explosion of population, transport, and communications – as well as hunger for resources – brought a new era of European imperialism: no longer simply the conquest of temperate climates such as North and South American and Australia and New Zealand (all "neo-Europes"), but also the carving up of the rest, South and East Asia and Africa.

The industrial revolution turned diversity into division. What might otherwise have been different paths of development – or small differences in timing on the same path – now became an unbridgeable gap.

You might think that if the 21st Century was to be an age of ecological reckoning, then the 20th Century – which brought previously unheard of levels of material prosperity to more people than ever before – would have been a century of peace. On the contrary: it was a century of devastating war. Privileged classes carried their illusions of heroism and chivalry into mechanized slaughter in the First World War. The battle of Verdun in 1916 killed a million; the British offensive on the Somme cost Britain 60,000 on the first day of the attack. As Eric Hobsbawn puts it in *The Age of Extremes,* men lived like, and with, lice and rats in the water-logged trenches, behind sandbags, under artillery shelling, and emerged to be mowed down by what Ernst Junger called a "hurricane of steel" of machine-gun fire. Not more than one in three French soldiers came through the war without harm. One quarter of the Oxford and Cambridge students under twenty-five who served were killed. Germany lost 1.8 million.

Hobsbawn asks why the First World War could only be totally won or totally lost. His answer is that "in this war, unlike earlier wars, which were typically waged for limited and specifiable objects, was waged for unlimited ends. In the Age of Empire, politics and economics had fused. International political rivalry was modeled on growth and competition, but the characteristic feature of this was precisely that it had no limit." More specifically, war's toll upon the whole society meant that it required mobilization of the whole civilian population – and thus an absolute ideological justification.

The First World War never really ended. The armistice brought a punitive peace, which the Allies imposed on Germany, sowing seeds for the next war. And total war against a truly evil Nazi Germany persuaded President Franklin Roosevelt to develop atomic weapons, which the United States used against a largely defeated Japan in an effort to intimidate the Soviet Union – but of course with the effect of drawing the U.S.S.R. into a nuclear arms race.

Nuclear weapons – originally an American monopoly – threatened global annihilation during the Cold War and persuaded civilized people that safety depended on preparing to bring on a catastrophe that would have destroyed civilization. Nuclear weapons live on to threaten the post Cold War world with disastrous regional wars and nuclear terrorism. Perhaps our willingness to court ecological disaster is in part their legacy as well.

Why did the Cold War end peacefully with the triumph of the West? Perhaps it didn't. The Soviet Union did collapse under the weight of seventy years of dictatorship and a rigid command economy. Its restless subjects – and even more, those of satellite states – were seduced by Western advertising, and then bitterly disillusioned by the actual results of privatization.

The American pundit Francis Fukuyama declared: "What we may be witnessing is not just the end of the Cold war... but the end of history as such: that is, the end point of mankind's ideological evolution and the universalization of Western liberal democracy as the final form of human government."

Fukuyama was not claiming an end to history in the literal sense that events, including unpleasant ones, would somehow stop happening. His claim was closer to Margaret Thatcher's favorite acronym: TINA: "there is no alternative" – no alternative to the economic free market (or more accurately, corporate capitalism) and Western democracy.

For Fukuyama, as for 20th Century French philosopher Alexandre Kojeve, "Human history and the conflict that characterized it was based on the existence of contradictions: master and slave, the transformation and mastery of nature, the struggle for the universal recognition of rights, and the dichotomy between proletarian and capitalist. To say [as Hegel had] that history ended in 1806 with Napoleon's victory at the Battle of Jena meant that mankind's ideological evolution ended in the ideals of the French or American revolutions: while particular regimes in the real world might not implement these ideals fully, their theoretical truth is absolute and cannot be improved upon."

Twenty years later, it is apparent that history did not end – and not just in the obvious sense of September 11, 2001 and the ideological struggle between the West and Islam. More importantly, something cannot be inevitable if it is also impossible, and the global capitalism that Fukuyama celebrates turns out to be unsustainable. If today's world has the equivalent of 280 billion ghost-slaves, bringing the rest of the world to American levels would raise that number to above a trillion. Global warming is more than a crisis of how "we" undifferentiated humans live on this planet: it is crucially a matter of equity and history.

Cultural differences might have been a matter of diversity but not necessarily of division and conflict. It was imperialism, industrialization, and globalization that at once forced everyone into a single competition and transformed fluctuating fortunes into an irreversible gap. Of course, empires fall and new powers emerge. But a growing middle class leaves a persistent underclass ever more precarious, no longer self-sufficient in an impoverished and marginalized country, and equally marginal in the vast slums of megacities. It is the London of Dickens and Blake with no hope of relief or progress.

The democracy which Fukuyama took as the flattering political form of the end of history, to match its corporate capitalism, depended on economic growth. As Hobsbawm writes: "Where governments have enough to distribute to satisfy all claimants, and most citizens' standard of life is rising in any case, the temperature of democratic politics rarely rises to fever pitch." This was the case during the prosperity following the Second World War. But in the 1930s, "Faced with insoluble economic problems and/ or an increasingly revolutionary working class, the bourgeoisie now had to fall back on force and coercion, that is to say, on something like fascism." Or at least this was the Left's view and, as Hobsbawm says, it has a "core of truth" although it applies to

Germany rather than to Britain and the United States, which escaped the crisis democratically through Keynesian economics – that is, through government spending to revive the economy. That path was not open to the Weimar Republic, which was subject to the punitive economics of Versailles. Whether it is open to contemporary democracies in an age of corporate and financial globalization remains to be seen.

Economic growth offered a substitute for social justice. In its absence, conflict could not be contained. "The Weimar Republic fell largely because the Great Slump made it impossible to keep the bargain between state, employers, and organized workers which had kept it afloat." In 1932, the combined vote of communists and Nazis polled an absolute majority. The old Establishment, disliking both, unhesitatingly chose fascists.

As postwar prosperity ebbs in a world where a few hundred billionaires make as much as do a billion people, where some water their golf courses and others lack clean water, Fukuyama's claim that the ideals of the American and French revolutions are the last word and the end of history, appears at best deluded. We are not at the end of history, because while the ideals of political democracy in the American and French revolutions were not mere ideology for capitalism, they were blind to its limits: nature and community.

To date, history is schizophrenic: it is a tale of freedom and exploitation. Marx saw communism as the synthesis of this dialectic, but that synthesis was based on the assumption that natural resources were infinite. Fukuyama saw in the collapse of communism a vindication of bourgeois democracy, the end of history, almost the purpose; but when the bubble burst, so did certainty.

What happened in history? What happened to history?

How did an unsustainable civilization triumph over others that could have made peace with the Earth for millennia? Western culture – which was in fact an amalgam of many cultures – was doubly potent in its mixture of raw power and freedom. But now global warming makes energy a source of conflict rather than an escape from it: the very use of energy now puts people at risk, the poor and vulnerable most of all. Meanwhile, our ability to extract fossil fuels has peaked and what remains will be much more expensive. Growth was an automatic pilot, avoiding the question of who gets what. We have come not to the end of history but to its turning point. It remains to be seen where and how we shall turn: to empire and exclusion, to chaos, or to a new global and local social compact.

4 The Ends of Certainty

Humans' fantasies about robots preceded robots themselves – by more than two thousand years. In her fascinating book *Gods and Robots,* Adrienne Mayor tells of Talos, the robotic monster guardian of Crete. As recounted by Appolodorus of Rhodes in *Jason and the Golden Fleece,* the giant bronze humanoid patrolled the coast of Crete and hurled boulders at intruders. He could also crush them in his remorseless metallic embrace. Jason, however, formed an alliance with Circe, who bewitched Talos long enough to loosen a bolt in his ankle and open the cap, upon which his life fluid flowed out and he expired.

The fascinating thing about this ancient science fiction is that a supernatural story, which could have featured Talos as an ordinary mythical giant, instead features an imaginary device. Long before such a machine was possible, the idea of a wondrous machine caught the imagination more powerfully than that of a merely supernatural giant.

What is it about machines that makes them the stuff of fantasy, especially for overgrown boys? As a diplomat's son, who almost grew up on airplanes, I used to ask my father, "Which do you prefer, Daddy, a 707 or a DC-8?" The airplanes were astonishingly similar, as my father would explain in reply, yet there was no doubt in my mind that at some point he would admit the superiority of the Boeing, perhaps for its sharper, more masculine lines. Likewise, the frequent breakdowns of our family car were to my four year old self delightful emergencies; I leave the interpretation to Sigmund Freud.

The fascination of the mechanical lies, I think, in the idea of manipulation. When the machine naturally or unnaturally invaded the territory of the living – when, that is, it becomes an android, we become as gods.

"It is the business of intelligence to suborn people." The words belong to Allen Dulles, head of the C.I.A. at the height of the Cold War, whose watch included the 1953 coup to overthrow Mohammad Mossadegh in Iran. Francis Bacon, Attorney General, Privy Councilor, and Lord Chancellor to King James I, apparently agreed – not only in affairs of state but in his enormously influential exposition of the scientific method. "For like as a man's disposition is never well known or proved till he be crossed, nor Proteus ever changed shapes till he was straitened and held fast, so nature exhibits herself more clearly under the trials and vexations of art [mechanical devices] than when left to herself."

Bacon's defenders deny that he advocated torturing nature. The famous phrase "putting nature to the rack" in fact belongs to his brilliant admirer Gottfried Leibniz, co-discoverer with Isaac Newton of the calculus and philosopher whom Voltaire satirized for his doctrine that we live in the best of all possible worlds. Feminist scholars such as Carolyn Merchant are persuasive that sexual, sometimes sadistic imagery pervaded the terms in which the men of the 17th Century imagined modern science. Merchant quotes Bacon: "For you have but to follow and as it were hound nature in her wanderings and you will be able to lead and drive her to the same place again" The metaphor is from hunting dogs, and it stresses the role of intrusive experiments in producing the replicable results which are the foundation of modern science.

Critics of the deterministic, mechanistic model do not deny that it "works." Rather, they warn that it works dangerously well – in other words, it has lethal unintended consequences. Yet we have also discovered its limits: the points where prediction begins to fail. As cracks have appeared in the old, deterministic paradigm, we have begun to see limits that are also the opening to an alternative paradigm that centers on life.

In school we learn the heroic story of Galileo's conflict with the Catholic Church. The battle between dogmatic religion and science continues today in fundamentalist denials of evolution and climate change. Even more important, however, was the alliance of organized religion and science in persecuting nature cults and women healers, who were denounced and executed as witches. Approximately 100,000 women were tried for witchcraft in Europe. Misogynists associated witchcraft not only with women's supposed lust and magic but also with social chaos and doctrinal heresy. Shakespeare's *Tempest* reversed Montaigne's utopian vision of the New World and painted the native Caliban as an uncouth savage with a wicked witch, Sycorax, as his mother.

In *A World Without Women,* historian of science David Noble charts "the Christian Clerical Culture of Western Science," to cite its subtitle. The story begins in the Second Century. Misogynist monasticism did not simply follow from Jewish and Roman patriarchy. Early Christianity itself, though contradictory, promised a new world transcending gender differences and hierarchy. The Roman Empire transformed Christianity even before adopting it. In the face of persecution, an ascetic male clergy bent on controlling its followers and – less successfully – human desire gave the Church its antifeminist cast, which would last almost two thousand years. Noble writes that "Benedictine monasticism, with its emphasis on law, regularity, discipline, and obedience, was made to order for Pope Gregory, who aimed to "establish in the place of the vanishing empire the temporal power of the papacy." (Noble, p.85) For centuries, however, much of the clergy in Europe was married. After the Viking raids destroyed English monasteries in the Ninth Century, King Alfred and King Edgar at the end of the Tenth rebuilt them for celibate males and, to a much lesser extent, for cloistered women. Likewise Pope Leo IX began reforming – that is, purging – the Continental church, beginning in 1049. Noble recounts the Twelfth Century tragedy of Abelard and Heloise, whose love was punished with Abelard's castration and Heloise's isolation in a convent.

The great medieval universities of Paris and Oxford were initially clerical institutions. New College, Oxford, for example, is St. Mary's College of Winchester in Oxford, a "chantry" whose until recently all-male scholars were charged to pray for the soul of the founder, William of Wykeham, Bishop of Winchester and Chancellor of England. Noble writes that Paris and Oxford enthusiastically revived classical and Aristotelian misogyny – though ironically the Islamic scholar from whom they learned their Aristotle, Ibn-Rushd or Averroes, strongly believed in the "natural similarity, or social equality, of men and women." (p.157)

Late medieval scholar-theologian pioneers of science, such as Robert Grosseteste and Roger Bacon of Oxford, saw astronomy, astrology, medicine, mathematics, optics, and even automata, as vindicating "an essentially Augustinian pursuit of salvation through faith." (164) The point is not whether discoveries were made in religious terms: you could argue that only such terms could legitimize introducing something new and potentially subversive. The important influence was not of religion in itself. It was that of a religion that worshiped ascetic control upon a science framed in ascetic, mechanistic, and deterministic terms. This influence became even clearer as centuries passed, with the Calvinist doctrine of predestination and the scientific one of determinism. "The mechanism of God and the mechanism of matter," writes Alfred North Whitehead, "were the twin monstrous issues of limited metaphysic and clear logical intellect." (*Science and the Modern World,* p.85.)

The God who set the terms for Western science was a transcendent Creator "at whose fiat the world came into being and whose imposed will it obeys." Whitehead continues: "When the Western world accepted Christianity, Caesar conquered, and the received text of Western theology was edited by his lawyers." (*Process and Reality,* p.404) It was this authoritarian culture which conducted medieval animal trials were, as historian of science Joseph Needham notes, freaks of nature such as egg-laying cocks were tried, sentenced, and executed as offenses against divine law. Needham, a scholar of Chinese science, notes that in China the cocks might simply have quietly disappeared as blemishes upon cosmic harmony – but without the rigor of explicit, positive law.

Galileo, for all his reputation as a heretic, was educated in a monastery and then at the University of Pisa. He adopted – rather belatedly – the Church's ascetic misogyny, forsaking his lover and the mother of three of his children; and in 1610, he left the Venetian Republic to live at the court of Cosimo de Medici in Florence. He wrote that he sought the freedom – from complexity, at least – of living under an absolutist ruler. (Noble 216-7)

Mechanistic science was an escape from freedom – a brilliant rejection of the confusing complexity of the real world for mathematical, deterministic simplicities. Pre-scientific thought had been animistic: it saw everything – not only animate but also inanimate – as having initiative. The crucial distinction in Aristotelian physics was between rest and motion, and the crucial metric was velocity. As Whitehead notes in *Science and the Modern World,* Galileo understood that "the crucial point to attend was not the motion of bodies but the changes of their motions." (p.46.) Galileo's insight became Newton's First Law: "Every body continues in its state of rest, or of uniform motion in a straight line, except so far is it may be compelled by force to change that state." *(Ibid.)* What matters is no longer motion; it is acceleration. Acceleration indicates that a force is acting upon an object. The world is simplified into inert objects subject to forces (notably, gravity) according to laws which were deterministic, predictable, and manipulable. Ironically, though, in shifting attention from motion to change in the rate of motion, Galileo and then Newton also introduced the concept that information depends on difference – a principle of cybernetics that would lead away from the crude mechanism of inert matter governed by inexorable forces as the incarnation of divine law.

The genius of Seventeenth Century science lies in its abstraction. In the real world, there is a difference between rest and motion. Objects do not simply stay in motion – or you would have perpetual motion. They come to a halt because of friction. Steady motion, therefore, is not mere inertia as in Galileo and Newton's law. Galileo and Newton brutally isolated the system under study from distracting complications: this allowed Newton to formulate laws of force, mass, and acceleration (notably in the Second Law: F = ma, the force is equal to the mass times the acceleration; or, the acceleration will be the quotient of the force divided by the mass upon which it acts). "The great forces of nature, such as gravitation," Whitehead writes, "were entirely determined by the configuration of masses. Thus the configurations determined their own changes, so that the circle of scientific thought was entirely closed." (*SMW*, p.50.)

Newton brilliantly unified the motion of the planets in their orbit with the fall of an apple here on Earth: both were obeying gravity. Ilya Prigogine and Isabelle Stengers, in *Order Out of Chaos,* quite a 1728 poem by J. T. Desaugliers:

Nature, compelled, his piercing Mind obeys,

And gladly shows him all her secret Ways;

'Gainst Matematicks she has no Defence,

And yields t'experimental Consequence.

Here the sexual and sexist language celebrates mechanistic science. It is at once passively deterministic and actively manipulative. The contradiction stems from the scientist's God's-eye view.

Lewis Mumford in *The Pentagon of Power* accuses Galileo of "a crime far graver than any of the dignitaries of the Church accused him of; for his real crime was that of trading the totality of human experience, not merely the accumulated doctrines of the Church, for that minute portion which can be observed within a limited time-span and interpreted in terms of mass and motion, while denying importance to the unmediated realities of human experience." (p.57.) The world of human experience – taste, touch, scent, and even more our thoughts and feelings – is exiled, demoted to secondary status. For centuries, scientific progress was defined as the extension of this reductionist science to explain – or explain away – more and more phenomena, from physics to chemistry to biology to genetic engineering and artificial intelligence.

While Galileo and Newton reduced nature to inert mass and force, Descartes took philosophy on a similar – though much less productive – quest for certainty. Descartes is often remembered for his insistence on doubting everything that cannot be proved. But as Stephen Toulmin shows in his book *Cosmopolis,* the skepticism of Descartes was antithetical to the humanist skepticism of this Sixteenth Century predecessor Montaigne. Montaigne rejected certainty; Descartes rejected everything that was not certain. Montaigne embraced the world, in all its ambiguity; Descartes embraced certainty and accepted only an artificial world reconstructed with the Cartesian method. To him animals were mere machines, and so were humans except in their self-conscious intellect. With reality so split, later mechanists would propose that consciousness itself is an illusion, a mere byproduct.

In searching for the reasons for what he calls "the Seventeenth Century Counter Renaissance, Stephen Toulmin compares Henri IV's assassination on May 14, 1610 to the assassination of John f. Kennedy on November 22, 1963. Henri of Navarre had been a Protestant who accepted Catholicism with the immortal words, "Paris is worth a mass." But in doing so, he took care to preserve the rights of Protestants – for example, in the Edict of Nantes, where he "codified and regularized the position of his Protestant citizens." (p.49.) Toulmin suggests that Henri's commitment to a tolerant state with freedom of religion was parallel to the interest of Henri's friend Montaigne in living with uncertainty.

With the assassination of Henri and with religious wars in Germany in the 1620s, powerful Europeans concluded that both

Henri's political and religious tolerance and Montaigne's philosophical pluralism were failures. The Thirty Years War (1618-48) killed eight million, including many civilians as rape and pillage wracked the Continent. If religion led to such chaos and strife, perhaps the absolute certainty of mathematics offered a secure realm. Toulmin suggests that Henri's murder spurred Descartes and his contemporaries to embark on a search for certainty though what they imagined to be a rigorous logical method that they supposed was beyond challenge.

"Cartesian dualism" has become a standard term for the opposition of matter and spirit. Matter is conceived as dead, inert, and predictable by rigorous deterministic science. Spirit – the world of the mind – is the supposed domain of free will.

Though conventional, this set of oppositions between deterministic matter and free spirit is deeply misleading. Though there are no completely deterministic systems in an unfolding cosmos, some symbolic systems such as mathematics come close. A computer can beat a chess grandmaster but loses to a three year old in the advanced art of making mud pies. Our consciousness, our creativity, and our freedom are bout up with our materiality and finitude. "Et in Arcadia ego" ("I, Death, am also in Arcadia" belongs to Death, or at least to our awareness of it. But though these insights are central to Shakespeare, they were foreign to mechanistic science, the sterile world created for fear of life and its complexities.

"Cosmopolis" itself as a word refers to the classical idea of unity of the cosmos and the state: the order of nature should be a guide to the appropriate order for human society. The idea was revived in the Renaissance. Toulmin suggests that as Henri's assassination changed people's ideas of what was politically possible, it influenced their idea of the order of nature as well.

While the idea of a "philosophy of nature" has been out of favor in any explicit form in more recent thought, I believe that in an age of ecological crisis the relation between the order of nature and that of society is a central question. Addressing it is precisely the effort that this book undertakes.

The royal absolutism that Descartes endorsed met its fate in France in 1789, but the intellectual absolutism in science was hugely successful and defined modernity itself. The Eighteenth and Nineteenth Centuries transformed life through the rapid growth of cities, the destruction of handcrafts for a factory system, and the increasing role of machines. Until the late Nineteenth Century, technological innovations were the more the work of practical inventors than applications of mathematical scientific theory coming from a university laboratory. The spread of dark satanic mills, as William Blake called them, both popularized the mechanistic outlook and sparked a Romantic reaction to it. But whether it was the machine-breaking of Luddites or Keats's charge that Newton had unwoven the rainbow, the protest seemed to mainstream culture a doomed last stand, romantic in the sense of impractical, by "rebels against the future." (The phrase is indeed the title of David Noble's book on the Luddites, though he uses it ironically to suggest that they were offering an alternative vision of the future, not rejecting the future altogether. Indeed Noble argues that they have much to teach us.)

Ironically, however, machines themselves raised problems in science that undermined the Newtonian world view. "Machine" is one of the most complex words in the Indo-European languages. In "machination" there is the sense of a plot. "Machine" is descended from Greek *mekhos,* "a contrivance" and related to Germanic *magan* "to have power" as in "may." Automata indeed seem magical, at once possessing and lacking autonomy. Early uses of "machine" in English refer to engines of war, and ever since Archimedes there has been a close connection. In practice, machines are of two kinds: power tools and automata. A saw is a tool; a power saw is considered a machine. A clock, even if run with weights and a pendulum or a spring rather than with electric power, is a quintessential machine.

Yet amid the intoxications of small boys and large industrial societies playing with machines, two awkward issues arose. The first is that fuel runs down. The second concerns the nature of self-regulation. Perpetual motion is the ultimate fantasy of an entirely closed system. In practice, you must wind a clock and stoke a furnace. Yet in a perfectly Galilean, perfectly Newtonian world, there would be nothing impossible about perpetual motion. As we saw, Galileo's stroke of genius was to ignore the difference between rest and motion and insist that only change in the rate of motion mattered and indicated the operation of a force upon a mass. In practice, however, friction brings moving bodies to a stop unless there is a continued application of power.

The defining machine of the Nineteenth Century, the steam engine, raised both the thermodynamic and the cybernetic problem – the issues of time and of control – and thus began to undermine Newtonian mechanism. An ideal engine would transfer all its thermal energy into mechanical energy, and this mechanical energy could be used to restore thermal energy (as for example by compressing a gas), and thus the cycle would be closed. But as Sadi Carnot observed in 1828, no machine is perfectly efficient, and he attributed this loss to the propagation of heat. Thus, in practice if not in yet theory, irreversibility entered science with thermodynamics. In 1865, Rudolf Clausius introduced the decisive concept: entropy. His two laws of thermodynamics are:

- The energy of the universe is constant.
- Its entropy tends toward a maximum.

Entropy is not a measure of energy in itself but of the loss of information or order. Heat (energy, that is) is not destroyed but it is dispersed, so that it is no longer in a useful form. And this change is irreversible. If you open an oven door, you don't see heat leave the room to concentrate in the oven; neither does a cup of stirred coffee suddenly turn back into black coffee and cream rising back up to the creamer.

Irreversible change – the arrow of time – is universal outside the pages of science fiction – and of Newtonian physics. In theory, each of the millions or billions of collisions of molecules or atoms is reversible, so, on a microscopic level, there is no reason the coffee and cream only mix or perfume molecules only disperse. The standard answer is that the arrow of time is simply an arrow of probability. Things move from an improbable state of concentration to a more probable one of dispersion – or at least they do with such overwhelming probability that we take it for a law. Yet this flow of energy is not a mere description: you can use it to heat the boiler of a steam engine and run a locomotive or to explode gasoline in the cylinder of an internal combustion engine to drive a car. Thus science was forced to accept that the emergent behavior of populations is just as fundamental as the deterministic and theoretically reversible behavior of isolated bits of matter.

James Watt's steam engine included a governor or speed limiter – in this case a centrifugal device with fly-balls. Centrifugal force would drive the fly-balls up as they spun faster; this reduced steam, in turn limiting speed. Like any regulatory device, a governor employs the principle of feedback. Contrary to American common usage, where "negative feedback" simply means criticism and "positive feedback" means praise, in cybernetics "negative feedback" refers to a self-corrective device such as a thermostat which compensates for divergence from its set point. If the house is set at 65 degrees and the temperature falls to 60, the heat switches on; when it then rises to 70, the heater switches off. (The device must have an overshoot or bracket or it would switch on and off incessantly.) Positive feedback by contrast amplifies difference: if the stock market falls steeply, investors panic and it becomes a crash. If global temperatures rise and permafrost melts, methane in the permafrost is released, sending a powerful greenhouse gas into the atmosphere and driving global warming further. Any natural system such as an ecosystem or a single living organism is a cascade of finely balanced *loops* of negative and positive feedback. Without negative feedback, an organism could not maintain homeostasis or steady-state; without positive feedback, it could not grow and change. Uncontrolled positive feedback is pathology. Much of this understanding would not come until the Twentieth Century, and we shall return to the discussion in later chapters, but already in the mid Nineteenth Darwin's colleague and co-discoverer of evolutionary theory Alfred Russell Wallace compared evolution to "a machine with a governor." (By the "governor" Wallace meant natural selection.)

Meanwhile, in the early Twentieth Century, Newtonian physics met its most decisive setbacks. Two centuries earlier Alexander Pope had written for Newton's epitaph:

> Nature, and Nature's laws, lay hid in Night;
>
> God said: Let Newton be; and all was Light.

How ironic, then, that Newton met his end over the nature of light itself.

Light famously exhibits some of the properties of waves and some of the properties of particles, and physicists split into rival camps, neither entirely successful. It occurred to the German physicist Max Born that both might be right, but in different ways: light was not made up of waves; instead waves described the probability of where a particle of light was to be found.

But where was that (not just in the case of a photon of light but of any subatomic particle)? In our familiar macroscopic world, an object's position can be determined. We take this for granted, but in strict scientific terms, this determination requires measurement. In the subatomic world, such measurement is no longer trivial. Werner Heisenberg formulated the famous Uncertainty Principle: You cannot simultaneously know the particle's position and its momentum: the more precisely you determine the one, the more inexactness creeps into the other. In the words of American physicist Henry Stapp, explaining it half a century later: "The particle must be isolated in order to be defined, yet interacting to be observed."

Another founder of Quantum Physics, the Danish physicist Neils Bohr, explained that every act of measurement disturbs the object measured to some extent. The difference in Quantum Physics is that this disturbance is decisive. The particle is so small that you cannot measure it with anything significantly smaller, so the impact is significant. There is no such thing as disembodied observation, the idealized God's eye view upon which Newton's certainty depended. The world as we know it consists, not of isolated objects in obedience to deterministic laws, but rather of interactions. To return to the words of Allen Dulles, the CIA Director: "It is the business of intelligence to suborn people." The quest for certainty is equally falsifying. Or, in William Blake's words: "We murder to dissect."

But Bohr was also eloquent upon the complementarity of the Quantum world and the familiar one. What then makes Quantum Physics a Holy Grail yielding greater insights into reality than a room filled with tables and chairs? One is reminded of the lazy schoolboy Winston Churchill, whose schoolmaster was trying to teach the Latin First Declension. He had taken as his example the declension of *mensa,* "table," as his example. They came to the vocative case. "What does that mean?" asked the impertinent Churchill. "Oh table," said the schoolmaster. "It is what you would use in addressing a table." "But I never do," replied Churchill.

The world does not just consist of tables and chairs, however, or of the inert objects which passively obey the laws of Newtonian physics. The idealizations of Newtonian physics were not simply false, or they would not have been powerfully predictive in, for example, astronomy and engineering, but they were the more powerful for being partial. They omitted the uncertain world which we find not only at the extremes of subatomic physics but more importantly in the intimate world that matters to us, from the instability of climate, to workings of our brains, to the interplay of our relationships, and the struggles of history.

May God us keep
From single vision
And from Newton's sleep. (Blake)

If nothing else, subatomic physics gives us permission to reawaken to the world that we know.

The world to our scale contains both the stable and the unstable, the inert and the reactive. The difference is not uncertainty on the micro-scale, which always exists; it is the context to amplify it, where the difference can make a difference. This is the brilliant achievement of physical chemist Ilya Prigogine in the thermodynamics of systems far from equilibrium – or, in lay language, in systems that can draw on free energy, like a spark hitting a barrel of gasoline instead of water, or an animal, whose metabolism (based on the energy derived from food) allows it to leap out of a tree. It makes possible self-organization without an outside, God-like engineer.

Paradoxically, this renaissance in science and human understanding has opened to us thanks to what at first seemed a tragedy: the clash of doctrines as Newtonian, mechanistic science encountered the limits of certainty. As Prigogine and Stengers remark, "The discovery of a physical impossibility is not a resignation to good sense; it is the discovery of an intrinsic structure of reality of which we had been unaware, and which condemns to impossibility a theoretical project." (p.220) Whether it is Rudolf Clausius's realizing that the inefficiency of machines was a reflection of time's irreversibility, or Einstein's recognition that it is impossible to travel faster than light and that space and time are relative, or Heisenberg's that you cannot simultaneously fix the position and momentum of a particle, or our own that our use of energy must have limits, encounters with impossibility compel us to redefine the problem, and our own goals, in a new and creative way.

Einstein famously distrusted Quantum Mechanics. "The theory delivers a lot," he wrote in 1926, "but hardly brings us closer to the secret of the Old One. I for one am convinced that *He* does not play dice." Here we see the theological stamp upon a modern physicist who could not cross the barrier to embrace creative uncertainty. Perhaps we should not even be looking for a "secret," a master equation written on a stone tablet, but for a web of relationships before our eyes and touching us at every point.

Meanwhile, we increasingly find ourselves caught in a web of machines. Science fiction features the robot that develops a will of its own. In real life, the most immediate danger is of a different kind.

On June 1, 2009, Air France Flight 447 from Rio to Paris encountered bad weather over the Atlantic. Ice clogged the tubes at the nose of the plane that its automated controls use to calculate the aircraft's speed. There was nothing wrong with the way the plane was flying, and it could have safely continued on autopilot. But it was programmed to shut down its automated system and hand over control to the human crew. The pilot was off duty. The two assistants, startled by their sudden responsibility, pushed their control sticks in opposite directions. The plane spiraled into the sea, killing everyone on board.

As David Mindell of M.I.T. argues in his book, *Our Robots, Ourselves,* "Air France 447 made tragically clear that as we constantly adapt to and reshape our surroundings, we are also remaking ourselves. How could pilots have become so dependent on computers that they flew a perfectly good airliner into the sea?" The problem, then, is not that robots with a will of their own take over. It is that when we rely so much on robots, we are unable to take over.

Likewise, it is humans, not drones, who are responsible for killing by drone strike. Yet the experience of killing by remote control is different for both the operators and the victims – and extremely stressful for both. Our notion of valor in war is based on reciprocity of risk. Take that risk away from the killer, and killing is sheer murder. It is the human meaning of technology that we need to think about. Machines do not bring certainty to an inherently uncertain world. As the great political activist and philosopher Antonio Gramsci remarked, "The old is dying and the new cannot be born. In this interregnum, a great variety of morbid symptoms appear."

5 The Universe for Beginners

I first thought about cosmology in a hurricane and revisited it in an ice storm. When we doubt the shelter that is our daily universe, it is the larger universe that becomes our home. When we lose electric power and artificial light, natural light and darkness again rule our lives. Darkness calls for stories. This is why non-industrial peoples consider cosmology a necessity.

When Copernicus shattered the Ptolemaic and Christian Earth-centered universe, the paradigm-shift went far beyond astronomy. Science, technology, and capitalism offered power at a price: estrangement. In the words of Jacques Monod: "Now at last does man realize that he wanders at the edge of an alien world, a world that is deaf to his music, just as indifferent to his hopes as it is to his suffering or his crimes." Monod actually relished what he took to be this harsh exigency.

The 21st Century universe is stranger than ever before. All ordinary matter and energy make just four percent of a universe apparently dominated by "Dark Matter" and "Dark Energy." We cannot, however, be said to "wander at its edge," because it is a universe without center. It is the loss of certainties that gives the universe a story. That story not only encompasses our own; it also illuminates it, because many of the same issues and principles stretch across its canvas.

The reason to study the universe is that it helps us to recognize our life right here, right now. "The subject matter could not be more fundamental," write Roberto Mangabeira Unger and Lee Smolin in their book *The Singular Universe and the Reality of Time.* "Cosmology is not just one more specialized science. It is the study of the universe as a whole, beyond which, for science, there lies nothing." Newtonian, deterministic science is based on isolating part of a system. That won't work with the universe. Cosmology is the proving ground of holistic thinking.

As Unger and Smolin assert, "Among the greatest and most important discoveries in recent times are discoveries about the universe and its history. The most important such discovery is that the universe itself has a history."

Cosmology, as they see it, is a battleground between what they call Timeless Naturalism and Temporal Naturalism. Timeless Naturalism, which has been the standard view in science, holds that the experience of time – with its passage and flow – is an illusion. Temporal Naturalism, by contrast, acknowledges that everything changes, even the laws of nature.

In the 1920s, the astronomer Edward Hubble discovered the galactic Red Shift. Light from distant galaxies is shifted to the red end of the spectrum – the more distant the source, the more so. This indicates they are receding from us – just as the pitch of the horn of a train rises as the train approaches and falls as it passes. Since the red shift applies across the horizon, it indicates the universe is expanding.

In 1965, the astronomers Penzias and Wilson discovered a strange background noise in their radio-telescope – one which they initially attributed to faulty equipment or even to nesting birds. It turns out instead to be background black body radiation of 3 degrees Kelvin (that is, 3 degrees above absolute zero), which is uniform to about one part in one hundred thousand throughout the universe. If the Red Shift tells us that the universe is expanding, the black body radiation appears to be a relic of the Big Bang, the explosion in which the inconceivably hot and dense primeval fireball blasted apart.

"The Big Bang" was originally a derisive term which the astronomer Sir Fred Hoyle applied to the theory of an initial explosion. Hoyle was a leading proponent of the steady state theory: that of an essentially changeless universe. Albert Einstein, revolutionary though he was in some respects, had an almost religious belief that time is an illusion, and like most astronomers before Hubble, he believed that the universe is essentially static. In the

General Theory of Relativity, he discovered that gravity can be described as the way mass bends space: starlight, for example, is bent as it passes the sun. The more mass in the universe relative to its size, the more gravity will draw the universe together until it collapses in a "Big Crunch." Alternatively, if total mass is less and thus gravity is weaker, the universe expands forever. Contrary to the predilections of Einstein and virtually everyone else at the time, the equations of General Relativity showed that the universe cannot stay constant. The universe must have had a beginning.

Why do we even have a universe? How could the universe emerge out of nothing? For millennia and still to many today, the answer was obvious: creation presupposes a Creator. However much progress science might make explaining the universe with deterministic laws, there could almost by definition be no natural explanation of how something could emerge from nothing. An eternal universe or an eternal God seemed to be the only possible solutions. Today our point of view is very different: our universe is an example of novelty, which continues within the universe long after its birth. "Perhaps the reason we have something instead of nothing," remarks astrophysicist Frank Wilczek, "is that Nothing is unstable."

In the beginning, all the mass and energy of the present universe was compressed into the size of a single particle. It was thus subject to the uncertainty of the quantum world, in which particles fluctuate into and out of existence, emerging from the chaotic quantum void as do particles. "Our universe does not need perfection to exist," writes Marcello Gleiser. "It needs imbalance."

Nobel Prize winning chemist Ilya Prigogine, a renaissance mind who is the greatest pioneer of understanding how order emerges from fluctuations, suggests how the universe might have emerged. If, as Einstein's General Theory of Relativity maintains, gravity is the way matter curves space, then in a pre-universe without energy-matter, there would be no gravity either. A quantum fluctuation in the pre-universe lends the universe matter-energy and a corresponding amount of gravity, since the overall energy of gravity is negative and compensates for the positive of energy-matter.

There are countless unanswered and perhaps unanswerable questions. Is ours the only universe? Why did the cosmos produce a universe capable of giving rise to life? If the fundamental numbers of the universe, such as gravity, which decreases with the square of the distance, the speed of light, or Planck's Constant, governing the size of atoms, were different, we would not be here, and life in any form might not exist. Does the universe, as String Theory posits, have hidden dimensions of which we are unaware?

The more exotic features of cosmology, such as the multiverse and hidden dimensions, have become part of popular culture. Unger and Smolin remark: "There are an infinite number of things that might be true of the universe, but which could never be observed. Multitudes of giant angels and unicorns might be hovering just outside our cosmological horizon. The dark matter might be tiny elves left over from the big bang."2

For Unger and Smolin, these exotic speculations are anything but the last word. "The growth of untestable scenarios about unobservable multiple universes or extra dimensions are a symptom of the need to change paradigms" from time-denying deterministic science. "The road back to reality, we suggest, begins by making two affirmations about nature: the uniqueness of the universe and the reality of time."

Is time a dimension, like space? In some respects, such as calculating velocity, this is a useful and powerful description. But time is not like space because we cannot look backward or forward. The most fundamental kind of uncertainty is our inability fully to predict or control the future, because the future is in part open. This is where the inescapably spatial model of "dimension" is inappropriate, and our proclivity to use it betrays the natural tendency of scientists and the rest of us to seek a God's eye, omniscient view. Marcello Gleiser believes that a fundamentally religious agenda inherited from Greek and Christian thought still shapes and distorts science in its search for super-symmetry and a Final Theory. Time is not like space – if there were no uncertainty, there would be no time, and if there were no time, there would be no uncertainty. Yet the universe itself emerged from uncertainty.

While perfect symmetries are beautiful to the eye of mathematical theorists, we owe our existence to an asymmetry: matter vastly exceeds anti-matter. "Had matter and anti-matter coexisted in equal amounts during early cosmic history," notes Gleiser, "they would have annihilated each other to such an extent that the Universe today would consist mostly of a bath of radiation." (114) The reason for this asymmetry is unexplained.

It is imperfection of symmetry that gives rise to structure, just as it is time's irreversible flow – entropy – which fuels the growth of complexity. From the enormously hot and dense early universe, our universe has had 13.7 billion years to expand and cool. In this time, the universe has gone from an initial bath of elementary particles and radiation to complex structures such as humans, made up of 30 billion billion billion particles (3 x 1028). Of course, we are neither the universe's destination nor its destiny, only a small part of it. But what can cosmology tell us about creative uncertainty – about the conditions that allow complexity to grow?

If Grand Unification is the Holy Grail of physics, diversification is the same of biology. In fact, complexity arises on many scales, not just biology, from galaxies to molecules and (sometimes) from molecules to organisms and ecosystems.

What has happened in fourteen billion years? On the one hand, the answer is very simple. The universe has expanded and cooled. This process has gone on highly uniformly. On the scale of the cosmos as a whole, matter, motion, and energy seem, as we have said, to be quite evenly distributed.

But there has been another – contrary – trend, of which we ourselves are a significant expression. It is the development of diversity. When the Inflationary Period ended following the cosmic fire-ball, there was only the undifferentiated soup of matter and radiation. Speaking of this moment, the physicist Stephen Weinberg says, "The universe is simpler and easier to describe than it ever will be again." To a physicist, such simplicity evokes nostalgia – though such a perfect world of physics had no physicists.

How do these apparently opposed trends relate to one another? If the universe could come into being spontaneously, can we understand how, within the universe, diversity could appear spontaneously? Why, at least in some places, has this diversity steadily increased with time?

Let us identify the two elements of diversity necessary to life and then see what in the large-scale development of the cosmos has favored their concentration. One is the structural diversity of matter: different kinds of atoms, molecules, cells, and organic species. The other is the fact that there is available energy, because energy is concentrated in some places within the cosmos. We are bathed in a stream of incoming solar radiation (i.e., sunlight) which is the energy-basis for life on Earth.

This diversity, which is so significant to us, does not contradict the large-scale uniformity of the cosmos which we have already noted. Large-scale uniformity can be gauged in terms of the overall distribution of galaxies within the cosmos. In those terms, the differences between the Sun and the Earth, or any star and its surrounding space, are but microscopic irregularities. But in our terms these differences matter a lot. The two trends are contrasting but not mutually exclusive. It is the smooth and steady cooling of the cosmos as a whole which actually makes possible the growth of diversity on which we depend and of which we are a development.

Ever since it was a primeval fireball, the universe has been freezing. "Freezing" is the central analogy and concept physicists use to describe the qualitative changes that take place at certain critical points of cooling. The universe has undergone a series of freezings in the course of its history.

What is a freezing? When water falls below the freezing point and becomes ice, it undergoes a state-change from liquid to solid. This is the most familiar example of what physicists call a "phase transition." By this they mean that ice (at 31o F) has some physically different properties from water (at 33o F).

The history of the cosmos as a whole is one of cooling. The falling cosmic temperature is a kind of "clock, cooling instead of ticking," as the universe expands. (Weinberg) This cooling makes possible various types of freezing or phase transition (not only the familiar liquid/ solid example). Each freezing marks the appearance of new ordered structures, more complex than what was possible at higher temperatures. Think of a snowflake with its six-sided pattern. Why are there no liquid or gaseous snowflakes? The reason is that matter in these states is too turbulent for the comparatively weak forces, holding the snowflake together, to prevail.

As living beings, we could not, of course, exist in an absolutely frigid world. The whole cycle of our activity is directed towards keeping ourselves warm and extracting the chemically-stored energy, in food, to maintain our metabolism. At the same time, our bodies incorporate complex molecules which would be immediately destroyed at the very high temperatures of the early universe. Life is the outgrowth of an increasingly delicate interplay between energetic and conservative processes. This is what we shall now trace in more detail.

The freezings that take place with falling cosmic temperature involve not only qualitative changes in the state of matter (e.g., water to ice) but also "the freezing of forces." When physicists speak of a force "freezing," they refer to a qualitative difference in the behavior of the force which appears when the temperature falls below a critical point.

What emerges with the freezing of forces is the diversity of forces we see in our world today. Physicists recognize four distinct forces in the current universe: the electromagnetic force, the weak force (governing radio-active decay processes), and the strong force (binding together the atomic nucleus), as well as gravity. As the different names imply, the four forces operate with different strengths and under different conditions. The strong force is immensely strong and operates over a submicroscopic range; the electromagnetic force is one one-hundredth that strength and operates over a potentially infinite range (think of the long range of radio waves).

But in the first instants of the universe, these differences among the four forces were not apparent. We can see this by working backward, as physicists like to do. When the universe was one ten-billionth of a second old (10-10 seconds), instead of the current four forces, there were only three. Electromagnetism was "unified" with the weak force. Earlier, at 10-35 seconds, many physicists believe that the strong force was "unified' with these two, so that the strong, weak, and electromagnetic forces all operated in approximately the same way. Physicists call this point the Grand Unification. The aim of physics has been to cover as much of nature as possible under the tent of a single mathematical equation. Homogeneity is good, diversity inconvenient, from this point of view. Our world contains too much diversity to fit any one mathematical equation. But the early universe? The prospect of finding symmetries not apparent in the current universe gives exceptional theoretical interest to the early universe when the cosmic temperature was extremely high, just as ultra high energy physics of supercolliders sheds light on the early universe.

Why should physical forces behave differently at different temperatures? The answer has to do with the nature of physical forces themselves. "Force" is a rather naïve way of understanding basic phenomena which are better conceived as interactions of characteristic subatomic particles. "If you think of two ice skaters throwing snowballs at each other as they pass," explains James Trefil, "you will realize that the exchange can result in a deflection in the skaters' paths – a deflection we could interpret as arising from the action of a force."

The four forces – electromagnetism, the weak force, the strong force and (more speculatively) gravity – are each defined by the exchange of one characteristic particle: the photon for electromagnetism, the weak boson for the weak force, the colored gluon for the strong force, and the graviton for gravity. It is the *difference* in these exchange particles (and in some cases their mass) which accounts for the differences in the forces – just as the skaters would be more or less deflected if they were tossing tennis balls or lobbing cannon balls. In the early hot universe, the energy of motion of the exchange particles was so high that by comparison their difference in mass (rest energy) was insignificant. This leveling at very high temperatures can't be understood in terms of familiar examples. It depends on velocities beyond the range of our experience.

The physicists' interest lies in the trek backwards towards very early times and very high temperatures, where they hope that a single Grand Unified Theory will explain the maximum number of phenomena. But the cosmos has been steadily moving in the opposite direction from the physicists: it is to the cosmos, rather than to the elegance of physics, that we owe our existence. Specifically, the "freezing out" or separation of forces provides a necessary basis of diversity without which matter could not have developed in increasingly complex forms and life could never have evolved.

As temperatures fell below threshold temperature, the differences among exchange particles began to become significant instead of trifling. The four forces began to act with different strengths, as we see today.

What is the consequence of a variety of forces? Consider an atom, for example. The electron is bound to the nucleus by the electromagnetic force. That nucleus is held together by the strong force operating over an extremely short range (much shorter than the electron's distance from the nucleus) and exerting an attraction more than one hundred times stronger. The electron can be detached from one atom to another; or the electromagnetic force can bind together two atoms in a molecule. These bonds can be formed and broken without affecting the much more tightly bound nucleus.

If all forces were of one strength and range, then you couldn't dissolve anything without dissolving everything. The world would be either a compact lump or else specks of particulate dust. In either case, there would be no structure. It is the diversity of forces which is a first precondition for relative invariance: the spectrum from the relatively stable, enduring things, at one end, to areas of greater change and flexibility. There can be no cup of coffee if the cup pours as easily as the coffee it must hold (or if the intended drink is itself made of clay). Relative invariance (or, if you prefer, relative variance) is one of those principles which explain how and why uncertainty can be creative and complex. It comes as a surprise in an intellectual culture that prizes extremes: all is changeless; all is change. Neither, actually; and let us give thanks for the diversity of rates. While this point of view is well supported by physics, it goes against the grain of many physicists' absolutist proclivities.

Likewise, the Platonic tradition in Western thought sees a dualism between form and matter, as if matter were mere clay upon which an engineer imprinted form. In fact, matter in all its messiness is essential to the creation of complex form. The grain of the wood, the clarity and luster of a stone, even its blemishes, embed it in something more fascinating than any deductive plan. Matter-energy is not static. Its imperfections are an invitation to further pattern on a larger scale.

There are two basic processes in the cosmos: expansion and contraction. They are often conceived as fire and gravity. Fire is obvious in the big Bang and the explosion outwards of the universe. The diffusion process can take place on any scale from the cosmos to a perfume bottle. Gravity by contrast is a very weak force which increases in proportion to the total mass. The mass of the perfume bottle is trifling, and so the gravitational attraction of the molecules is inadequate to contain the turbulent chaos of their diffusion. The universe is of course more massive than the perfume bottle, and the density of its known matter and energy are closely balanced, so that physicists have argued whether it would continue to expand or contract in a big crunch. (This debate has been superseded by the discovery that it is not only expanding but accelerating – leading physicists to posit Dark Energy, which would repel the elements of the universe from each other. It strangely matches the cosmological constant Einstein invented and then abandoned to modify the General Theory of Relativity.)

But we do not feed from cosmic fire, from the heat of the Big Bang; nor do we live in a cosmic broth of naked atoms. Instead it is local inhomogeneity which allowed simple atoms to clump into aggregates massive and dense enough to ignite as stars.

The furnace known as a star is a giant nuclear fusion reactor. The nuclear reactions that power this furnace are possible because they satisfy three conditions: there is available nuclear fuel; it is at sufficient density for the reaction to take place; and there is enough time for this process to occur.

The energy of nuclear fusion depends, first, upon the fuel. Hydrogen, the lightest and most common element in the universe, is fuel to a fusion reaction, and iron is an ultimate waste-product from which no further energy can be extracted. The transformations from hydrogen to carbon "burn" or release vast amounts of energy and ultimately yield inert stellar ash.

Before two hydrogen nuclei can fuse, releasing a large quantity of energy, they must collide at sufficient energy. (The two nuclei are positively charged and thus repel each other.) In the star, the particles have been accelerated through the repulsion barrier because they are at very high temperature. As pre-stellar dust contracts under gravitational attraction, pressure and temperature rise past the barrier, and fusion begins.

In the difference between stars and technological fusion reactors, we see the significance of scale. The violence of a thermonuclear reaction is contained in a star by the gravitational attraction which holds the star together. By contrast, the mass of the nuclear fuel in a human-built reactor is nowhere nearly enough to create a strong gravitational field.

The star is an arena where the forces of attraction are winning, drawing the prestellar dust more and more tightly together. Depending on the star's total mass, this process may end in a Black Hole: a region of space-time where gravity is so intense that not even a light-ray can escape. Yet short of this extreme, the gradual prevalence of gravity provides a natural wall for the star-as-fusion-reactor. The burning of nuclear fuel from hydrogen down to iron releases radiation, including the energy we know as sunlight.

The star succeeds where not only human technologies, but also the early cosmos, have been known to falter. We have said that prime requirements for nuclear fusion are density and temperature. If those exist in a star, they surely also existed in much greater degree in the early cosmos – millions of times hotter and denser than the hottest and densest star. Why did the cosmic furnace leave any fuel instead of burning it all to ash?

In fact, the early cosmos did synthesize some hydrogen into helium as well as traces of other light elements. But even this process is incomplete – hydrogen predominates in the cosmos – and cosmic nuclear burning went no further towards the ultimate slag, iron.

The reason is that the early, hot cosmos was expanding at a tremendous rate. The necessary conditions for nuclear fusion lasted only an instant. The star, on the other hand, is basically contracting. There are millions of years for the necessary reactions to take place.

Again, we have nesting Russian dolls: in an expanding universe, the concentration of matter in stars, and there, the kindling of new fire, new expansive and diffusive processes. This marks the emergence within the universe of inhomogeneity within the cosmos -- though on a cosmic standard these are small, local differences in a totality that is astonishingly homogenous. A principle of information theory is that information depends on difference: a green light is significant because it could have been yellow or red. The interplay of expansion and gravity is what teased out multiple levels of structure and complexity.

The stellar furnace yields the third precondition to inorganic and organic evolution: diversity in the types of matter. The early cosmos produced, as we have said, only hydrogen and helium and minute traces of other light elements. Yet our molecule "words" are composed of an "alphabet" of 92 different atoms, or at least those among them that have incomplete electron shells. The synthesis of elements up to iron took place – and continues to take place – in stellar fusion furnaces. Crucial among them is carbon, which is central to life. (The heavy elements beyond iron require an energy surplus to be cooked. They were cooked by an energy infusion in very hot, exploding stars. The energy surplus in such heavy elements can again be released through nuclear fission.)

We have been discussing stellar furnaces; and yet, we should remember, we have been outlining the results of cosmic "freezing" the appearance of new forces and new states of matter with falling cosmic temperature. These facts are contrastive but not contradictory. In fact, they are interdependent, and in this interdependence lies a central lesson of cosmology for creative uncertainty in other domains. We are creatures far from thermal equilibrium: we maintain ourselves in a flow of matter, energy, and information. We are at risk of freezing to death. Yet fire also kills us and turns us to dust. We owe our existence not to any quantitative extreme but to what in cosmic terms is a narrow range of physical conditions giving rise to an increasing range of structural possibilities.

Something New Under the Sun

"The more the universe seems comprehensible," writes the physicist Stephen Weinberg, "the more it also seems pointless." Weinberg has given the right answer to the wrong question. It is the question that has brought some to cosmology and others to religion – though by no means all who come to these are in search of a hidden designer.

Why is there something rather than nothing? This question has long been the ultimate argument for the existence of God. Scientists and philosophers have traditionally conceded that the question is outside science, and they have sometimes called it meaningless. Yet it is a fair question with a surprising twist: we were wrong to assume that nothing – a cosmic zero or zero cosmos – is the default position. As we have seen, the void is unstable. This recognition is both a tremendous breakthrough in thought and a challenge to both deterministic science and deterministic religion, which took the very existence of the universe as the "first argument" for the existence of a purposive creator, as well as an invitation to an open religion and science, no longer at war.

This is not to deny the power of predictions. Weinberg, who in his book *The First Three Minutes* reveals his relish for good cooking, uses a "recipe" to determine the ingredients – and by implication the structure – of the universe. Weinberg gives a "recipe" for the universe at 1/100th of a second into the Creation:

"A baryon number equal to one part in one thousand million, and a lepton number per photon uncertain but small; a temperature at any time greater than the temperature of 3 degrees Kelvin of the present radiation background by ratio of the present size of the universe to the size at that time."

"Stir well," advises the chef, "and place in an expanding universe, with a rate of expansion governed by the gravitational field produced by this medium." And *that,* he implies, will produce this universe. The determinist recipe specifies not only the items in the universe but also the allowed quantities of each. From this, the physicist hopes to predict the behavior of the universe as a whole: to determine its temperature and density at any given time in the past or future; and to say whether the universe will continue to expand or begin to recoil, ending in infinite fire. But physicists have been caught by surprise: it is not a formula which has determined the ingredients, but rather evidence of acceleration which has compelled them to revise the formula – specifically to add Dark Energy. There is a constant tension in science between prediction and the falsification of theories by awkward evidence and the scramble to devise new theories. In this interaction lie the scientific method's power and the key to the astonishing progress of science.

But while reductionistic science has been very successful in understanding the elements of the universe, what about its complex patterns and structures? Atoms are as numerous as – within each type – they are meticulously standard. And some of those most central to life are highly stable as well. Every breath you take contains an atom from Julius Caesar's dying breath when he said, "Et tu, Brute!" But the world has changed since Caesar's fall far more than the atoms of which it is made. Nor does an atom of Caesar's breath constitute your claim to fame. If you are breathing one of Caesar's last atoms, it stands to reason everyone else is too.

It is with the development of nested levels of organization – particles, atoms, molecules, cells, organs, organisms, ecosystems and societies – that order enters upon novelty. It is a story beyond the scope of cosmology but possible only because of it. The new cosmology is not only a story of how the universe began but also of why it is a universe for beginners, a universe that gives rise to further creativity.

The pre-modern world view saw the Earth, and humans, as the center and purpose of the universe, which was a divine creation by an anthropomorphic God. The modern Copernican world view reversed that: the Earth is not only not at the center, it's on the periphery, and humans are no better than a pathetic accident of cosmic history. The second view, however, is merely an inversion of the first.

Instead of being at the center, or the periphery, life exists at the interface. As Caleb Scharf argues in *The Copernicus Complex*, "Perhaps we could call it a "cosmo-chaotic principle," the place between order (from the original Greek kósmos, meaning a well-ordered system) and chaos. Its essence is that life, and specifically life like that on Earth, will always inhabit the border or interface between zones defined by such characteristics as energy, location, scale, time, order and disorder." Life itself has long been part of what created and maintained our habitable world. Now, this responsibility has fallen upon us, and while there is no prize from an external God, there is a reminder that whether or not we are alone, we are at the least unique, an expression of the creativity of our singular universe and the reality of time.

6 Designs on Evolution

Who's Afraid of Charles Darwin?

The word "uncertainty" appears nowhere in Charles Darwin's *The Origin of the Species,* a notable absence in a book which did more than any other to shake the old certainty that humans were the product of God's design. True, "chance" appears sixty-one times and "contingency" sixteen. But these are more about the mechanism of natural selection than they are any larger claim of evolution as a supreme example of creative uncertainty. Like all great pioneers, Darwin was Janus, pointing toward the new while himself subtly but significantly still caught in the old.

Few things do more to obscure the uncertainties in evolution than the absurd arguments of fundamentalists against it. Gladiatorial debates such as one held during a snow and ice storm in February 2014 at the Creation Museum in Louisville, Kentucky between Biblical literalist Ken Ham and "science guy" Bill Nye are equally comforting to both sides, and, like all polarizations, conducive only to conservative fundamentalism in both the scientific and the religious camps. If the "other side" can twist evidence (or simply ignore evidence) to argue that yes, after all, the world was created in eight days, then fierce Darwinism is everything that is not moronic. BILL NYE: "There are billions of stars. Mr. Ham, how could there be billions of stars more distant than 6,000 years if the world's only 6,000 years old?" Later in the debate, an audience member asked Ham whether there was anything that could change his mind. HAM: "The Bible is the word of God."

Climate deniers reject the overwhelming evidence that humans are responsible for climate change because they cannot imagine life without fossil fuels. Religious fundamentalists reject the overwhelming evidence for evolution because they cannot imagine how life could be meaningful without the literal truth of the Bible. More sophisticated scientists and theologians have learned how to compartmentalize scientific and religious truth, to argue that each exists independently. It's a useful maneuver that buys space and time for both, but it avoids the question: What is the meaning of evolution? Or does it even have one? Yet how can it not, if it is the truth of our story? Instead of showing a design or divine plan, or that humans are just gene machines, what is interesting about evolution is that it is the best model we have of how order comes from chaos, how the dazzlingly rich web of life emerges without a plan. To see this we shall have to build upon Darwin but go beyond strict Darwinism, not halfway back to "Intelligent Design" but further from it than one man, even one as original as Darwin, could go in a lifetime, and certainly further than his followers among scientific reductionists wish to go.

One of the ironies of the history of science is that with genetic reductionism, biology has suffered a bad case of physics-envy even though physics had moved on to post-reductionist quantum mechanics. Today, when someone darkly refers to an evolutionary explanation — say, for war, crime, or inequality — you can bet they have a reductionist explanation in terms of "selfish genes"; while if they breathlessly talk about quantum entanglement, you can guess they are idealists who look to world peace. Yet it is a long and probably misleading stretch to derive politics from physics, as misleading in its way as it was for the Founding Fathers to look for the equilibrium of Newtonian mechanics. The real battle ground, as in the 19th Century, is evolutionary biology — but one that has moved beyond the mid-Twentieth Century reductionism that still haunts popularizations. I do not want to sound like an opponent of scientific progress, which itself is a beautiful example of Creative Uncertainty. What I do want to emphasize is a shift from the model of a purely genetic "blueprint" to a model of evolutionary advance, known as the Extended Evolutionary Synthesis, in the embodied creativity of the developing organism.

In one of his best essays in *Natural History,* the great maverick evolutionist Stephen Jay Gould shows that William Jennings Bryan, the prosecutor in the infamous 1925 Scopes Trial in Dayton, Tennessee, was in fact motivated by something more than Biblical literalism, what journalist H. L. Menken called the "degraded nonsense which country preachers are ramming and hammering into yokel skulls." There was, to be sure, plenty of degraded nonsense. In the Scopes Trial, a teacher, John Scopes, was charged with the crime of teaching Darwinian evolution, illegal under Tennessee law in a public school. Gould was curious because Bryan, of course, was much more than the Scopes prosecutor: he was one of the great Progressives of the turn of the century, remembered for denouncing rapacious capitalism of the Gilded Age and pleading not to crucify the working classes on a cross of gold. He was also a champion of women's suffrage. Though Bryan had never accepted Darwinian evolution, neither had he bothered to oppose it until the First World War.

Bryan had read with alarm *Headquarters Nights* by eminent American entomologist (and evolution supporter) Vernon Kellogg. Kellogg was stationed during the war at Red Cross Headquarters in Belgium, in a "small gray town on the Meuse, just where the water pours out of its beautiful canon course through the Ardennes," next to the Headquarters of the German General Staff. There he had a unique opportunity to witness the world view of the German command. Theodore Roosevelt wrote in the preface: "The man who reads Kellogg's sketch and yet fails to see why we are at war, and why we must accept no peace save that of overwhelming victory, is neither a good American nor a true lover of mankind." Kellogg himself writes: "My 'Headquarters Nights' are the confessions of a converted pacifist." He was horrified by the crude evolutionary doctrine that German intellectuals used to justify the war. "The creed of the *Allmacht* of a natural selection based on violent and fatal competitive struggle is the gospel of the German intellectuals; all else is illusion and anathema." Although Theodore Roosevelt called this "the unspeakably dreadful moral and intellectual perversion of character which makes Germany at present a menace to the whole civilized world," it was not limited to Germany. In *The Sleepwalkers,"* his examination of how Europe went to war in 1914, Christopher Clark remarks on the widespread "readiness to accept war, conceived as a certainty imposed by the nature of international relations." (p.239)

Bryan blamed Darwinism for "that damnable doctrine of might makes right that had spread over Germany." He was equally shocked by capitalists' use of Darwinism. "In England and America, Darwinism's worst influence lay in its justification for industrial exploitation as an expression of natural selection." "By paralyzing the hope of reform, it discourages those who labor for the improvement of man's condition. Its only program for man is scientific breeding, a system under which a few supposedly superior intellects, self-appointed, would direct the mating and movements of the mass of mankind – an impossible system." The eugenics movement was indeed a major force in early 20th Century America, until it lost credibility because of the Nazi eugenics program and its own assumptions that Anglo-Saxons were superior to Southern and Eastern European immigrants fell out of favor.

It is one of the twists of political history that today's fundamentalists are no longer politically progressive. They are more likely to be Republicans who oppose "big government." They are more upset by people of color on welfare than by the hedge fund traders belonging to the top one percent of our new Gilded Age. As British political commentator George Monbiot notes, "Modern fundamentalists reject the science of Darwinian evolution and accept the pseudoscience of social Darwinism." (*Guardian* 28 October 2016) They are also not yokels; they use technology like the rest of us, and Ken Ham in the Creation Museum debate deployed every technique of academic debating to argue a position that no fair minded person could sustain. It was equal part rejection of modernism and a display of the subjectivity of the flavors of post-modernism. "Why is worldview important in science?"

asks the Creation Museum's "Answers" newsletter – but to take us to Genesis, not the Sorbonne.

Bryan was neither the first nor the last to confuse the crude Neo-Darwinism of red-in-tooth-and-claw with Darwinism itself. He must have only skimmed Vernon Kellogg's *Headquarters Nights*, because Kellogg tried to prevent that misunderstanding. "Altruism—or mutual aid, as the biologists prefer to call it, to escape the implication of assuming too much consciousness in it—is just as truly a fundamental biologic factor of evolution as is the cruel, strictly self-regarding, exterminating kind of struggle for existence with which the Neo-Darwinists try to fill our eyes and ears, to the exclusion of the recognition of all other factors." If these debates had ended a hundred years ago, they would be of only historical interest. But if you call your workplace "Darwinian," it means what it did then. Meanwhile, we have come to think of ourselves as "gene machines." Moreover, the crude distortions in popular culture reflect real if subtler debates in evolutionary thinking.

The Devil's Chaplain

"What a book a Devil's chaplain might write on the clumsy, wasteful, blundering low & horridly cruel works of nature!" remarked Darwin in an 1856 letter to Joseph Hooker. Darwin was discussing the reproductive habits of jellyfish. Did they take in spermatozoa by the mouth? -- shocking to Victorian prudery. "I hope it is not true that man is descended from the apes," a respectable Victorian is said to have remarked, "and that if it is, that it will not become widely known." But while the fear that Darwinism endangers sexual morality seems absurdly quaint, the enduring issue is the frigid mechanism of natural selection.

Darwin himself was far from a merely abstract thinker. Grandson of the famous manufacturer and Abolitionist Josiah Wedgewood, Darwin was appalled by the fear he saw in the face of a Brazilian slave. As ship's naturalist on the Beagle, he noticed the "pale French gray" haze, "tinted with a little blue" of the tropical atmosphere near Rio de Janeiro; he marveled at the symphony of night frogs and the aromatic leaves of camphor, pepper, cinnamon, and clove trees. Indeed one of the great strengths of Darwin comes from his difference from most biologists a hundred years later. He observed nature first hand; many later biologists worked in sterile laboratories and observed genetic manipulations in nude mice. The difference between Darwin's theoretical eclecticism and the Neo-Darwinians' orthodoxy stems in part from the puritanism of laboratory animals and the turn to molecular biology.

But Darwin himself was not a political innocent, and the plot is thicker than the story I used to believe of the misapplication of a purely scientific idea. In fact, as Adrian Desmond shows in *The Politics of Evolution,* and Piers Hale in *Political Descent,* the long period of "Darwin's Delay" between the time he recognized the truth of evolution and the rushed publication of *The Evolution of the Species* was one where he recast evolution. Modern neo-Darwinian reductionist Daniel Dennett's famous title, *Darwin's Dangerous Idea,* is in fact at least partly the story of how Darwin made Lamarck's "Dangerous Idea" safe for a Victorian capitalist audience, a fact noted with amusement by Karl Marx and by Darwin himself. He did not reach the insight of genius of natural selection through observation alone. It was, rather, a genius (in the old sense of spirit) of the time, something that makes it less surprising that his younger colleague Alfred Russell Wallace reached the same conclusion while lying sick with fever on Borneo, sent his manuscript to Darwin, and impelled Darwin, after years of delay, to claim his intellectual due, giving an address at the Royal Society and rushing *The Origin of the Species* into print.

Darwin fused his observational knowledge – his first hand observations of Galapagos finches – with an idea that didn't come from biology at all: Adam Smith's model of the free market.

Evolution – as against a fixed, one-time creation – was not a new idea in 1859. In a historical sketch, Darwin somewhat too generously credited Aristotle with the idea. During his stay on Sappho's island of Lesbos, Aristotle certainly noticed the subtle gradations of nature," sponges and sea squirts and jellyfish shading from animal to vegetable and from vegetable to animal." However, as Rebecca Stott shows in *Darwin's Ghosts,* Aristotle believed nature to be eternal and species perfectly designed – a notion fundamentally at odds with mutability. Darwin did not know the other Greek tradition, that of Epicurus and Lucretius, that had room for randomness and uncertainty. Had he known them, evolutionary theory might rest on a less contradictory intellectual foundation. Likewise the great Arab natural philosopher Jahiz, working in Baghdad about 850, saw the nets and webs, the interconnectedness of nature, but he took perfect divine creation and intelligent design for granted. Leonardo da Vinci, the artist of chaos and mutability, "knew that the gaps between layers of strata represented thousands of years of time and that this meant that the earth was incomprehensibly older than the Church proposed. But he did not contemplate species evolution as we now understand it." By the early 19th century, however, French biologists did understand that; they called themselves "transformists." Seen from the other side of the English Channel, these intellectual heirs of the French Revolution were also dangerous atheists and radicals.

Darwin's extraordinary insight came from very different intellectual roots. As Karl Marx remarked in a letter to Friedrich Engels in 1861: "It is remarkable how among beasts and plants Darwin rediscovers his English society, with its division of labor, competition, opening up of new markets, 'discoveries,' and Malthusian 'struggle for existence.'"

Like many insights of genius, Darwinian "Natural Selection" as he presented it in 1859 was a fusion of two ideas: selection and thus progressive modification of domesticated species by stock breeders, and Thomas Malthus' observation that a population left unchecked will grow geometrically, while resources can at best grow arithmetically, and therefore not all can survive. Ironically, although Malthus had written his *Principle of Population* to argue against the pefectability of man, Darwin saw in it an engine for the perfectability – or at least the development and adaptation – of species.

Biblical Creationism insists on the immutability of species. But a central fact of human culture – the domestication of plants and animals – shows that in practice we have long known better. As Darwin notes, "If selection consisted merely in separating some very distinct variety, and breeding from it, the principle would be so obvious as hardly to be worth notice; but its importance consists in the great effect produced by the accumulation in one direction, during successive generations, of differences absolutely inappreciable by an uneducated eye." Darwin cites William Youatt, an English veterinary surgeon, to say that selective breeding "enables the agriculturist, not only to modify the character of his flock, but to change it altogether. It is the magician's wand, by means of which he may summon into life whatever form and mould he pleases." Lord Somerville, speaking of what breeders have done for sheep, says: "It would seem as if they had chalked out upon a wall a form perfect in itself, and then had given it existence."

But stock breeding is the result of conscious human purpose, and Darwin's paradigm-changing insight was to see the natural "struggle for existence" as a virtual stock breeder. Here was where the dark observation of Malthus was so useful to Darwin. As Darwin remarked, "We behold the face of nature bright with gladness, we often see superabundance of food; we do not see, or we forget, that the birds which are idly singing round us mostly live on insects or seeds, and are thus constantly destroying life; or we forget how largely these songsters, or their eggs, or their nestlings, are destroyed by birds and beasts of prey; we do not always bear in mind, that though food may be now superabundant, it is not so at all seasons of each recurring year." "Of the many individuals of any species which are periodically born, but a small number can survive.... Owing to this struggle for life, any variation, however slight and from whatever cause proceeding, if it be in any degree profitable to an individual of any species, in its infinitely complex relations to other organic beings and to external nature, will tend to the preservation of that individual, and will generally be inherited by its offspring.." "This preservation of favourable variations and the rejection of injurious variations, I call Natural Selection."

Darwin himself called Natural Selection "the doctrine of Malthus applied with manifold force to the whole animal and vegetable kingdoms." Though he never used Adam Smith's phrase "the Invisible Hand," Darwin had been a medical student at the University of Edinburgh and was deeply influenced by the Scottish Enlightenment. He knew of Smith chiefly through a secondary work by Dugald Stewart. Adam Smith stresses that the individual, "by pursuing his own interest, frequently promotes that of the society more effectually than when he really intends to promote it. I have never known much good done by those who affected to trade for the public good." Or, as Dugald Stewart summarizes Smith: "The most effectual plan for advancing a people to greatness, is to maintain that order of things which nature has pointed out; by allowing every man, as long as he observes the rules of justice, to pursue his own interest in his own way, and to bring both his industry and his capital into the freest competition with those of his fellow-citizens. Every system of policy which endeavours, either by extraordinary encouragements, to draw towards a particular species of industry a greater share of the capital of the society than what would naturally go to it; or, by extraordinary restraints, to force from a particular species of industry some share of the capital which would otherwise be employed in it, is in reality, subversive of the great purpose which it means to promote."

Darwin, likewise, sees "the universal struggle for life" as responsible for "the whole economy of nature, with every fact on distribution, rarity, abundance, extinction, and variation." Darwin's debt to Smith does not in itself prove that anything is wrong with his biological insight; important patterns are shared in nature and human society. But Marx was right to complain that it is circular to use Darwinian Natural Selection as an argument for the Invisible Hand and libertarian politics. Indeed, though Darwin himself rarely spoke or wrote on politics, in an 1872 letter to Heinrich Fick, Darwin expresses his "fear that Co-operative Societies, which many look at as the main hope for the future, likewise exclude competition. This seems to me a great evil for the future progress of mankind."

But, as noted, the plot thickens. Evolution as secular idea begins not in 1859 but in 1809, with Jean Baptiste Lamarck, and his idea was rightly considered revolutionary. Long after Darwin's natural selection had been accepted, Lamarck's name, together with that of hapless Soviet biologist Lysenko, was a byword for bad science. Ironically, though, we are recovering from the scrubbing of the 20th Century Neo-Darwinian synthesis provided by conservative German biologist August Weissmann, and today Lamarck and his findings are no longer taboo. What is the difference from the orthodox Darwinism still promoted by establishment reductionists such as Richard Dawkins and Daniel Dennett, an orthodox version in sync with the "free market"? The concept of agency — of the organism's own role in shaping its future, not merely as the passive vehicle for genes shaped by natural selection.

What Marx did admire in Darwinism is that it had demolished teleology, the idea of purpose in nature.

Or had it? As Robert Richards of the University of Chicago points out, Darwin's theory was constructed on theological scaffolding. In the essay he wrote in 1844, fifteen years before *The Origin of the Species*, Darwin imagined natural selection on the model of a supreme being. "Let us now suppose a Being{224} with penetration sufficient to perceive differences in the outer and innermost organization quite imperceptible to man, and with forethought extending over future centuries to watch with unerring care and select for any object the offspring of an organism produced under the foregoing circumstances; I can see no conceivable reason why he could not form a new race (or several were he to separate the stock of the original organism and work on several islands) adapted to new ends. As we assume his discrimination, and his forethought, and his steadiness of object, to be incomparably greater that those qualities in man, so we may suppose the beauty and complications of the adaptations of the new races and their differences from the original stock to be greater than in the domestic races produced by man's agency."

Darwin's language is hauntingly similar to the classic statement of determinism by Pierre Simon Laplace, who imagined an omniscient demon: "An intellect which at a certain moment would know all forces that set nature in motion, and all positions of all items of which nature is composed, if this intellect were also vast enough to submit these data to analysis, it would embrace in a single formula the movements of the greatest bodies of the universe and those of the tiniest atom; for such an intellect nothing would be uncertain and the future just like the past would be present before its eyes."

Why does this origin of the concept of natural selection hold more than historical interest? Because if you imagine life "as if" it were the work of a supreme being, you will miss both its imperfections and its creativity and see it only as molded by an external force.

"The face of Nature," writes Darwin, "may be compared to a yielding surface, with ten thousand sharp wedges packed close together and driven inwards by incessant blows, sometimes one wedge being struck, and then another with greater force." Is Natural Selection a virtual silversmith, beating life into preexistent molds, forms shaped by established formulas of what would be the fittest? Stephen Jay Gould writes that Darwin's religious opponents have greatly exaggerated the role of randomness in his theory. Darwinian and especially Neo-Darwinian theory deploys chance tactically – to provide variation. But "Darwinism invokes randomness only to generate raw material. It agrees with the critics in arguing that the world's order could only be produced by a conventional deterministic cause – natural selection in this case." [Gould, Structure, 224.]

The Natural Theologians such as William Paley, whom Darwin had read as a young man, argued that life must be the work of a divine artificer. If you are walking on a heath and come upon a stone, you can suppose it had always been there, he writes. But if you come upon a watch, you must suppose that "There must have existed, at some time, and at some place or other, an artificer or artificers, who formed [the watch] for the purpose which we find it actually to answer; who comprehended its construction, and designed its use. (...) Every indication of contrivance, every manifestation of design, which existed in the watch, exists in the works of nature; with the difference, on the side of nature, of being greater or more, and that in a degree which exceeds all computation." This is still the position of religious advocates of Intelligent Design, which seems to be the opposite of Darwinism. The evolutionist and atheist Richard Dawkins titled one of his books *The Blind Watchmaker* to stress that the blind mechanism of Natural Selection is what produces organic structures as complex as if they had been designed.

Dawkins and Darwin are certainly right that there is no designer. The more important point, however, is that there is no design. Evolution is utterly different from a simulation of engineering. Both Dawkins and Darwin know that, but the cast of their thought leads to repeated misunderstandings in the public's view of evolution, and baits a new round of religiously based Intelligent Design, once again illustrating Alfred North Whitehead's warning that "the mechanism of God and the mechanism of matter were the twin monstrous issue of limited metaphysic and clear logical intellect." Or as biologist John Reiss writes in this book *Not By Design: Retiring Darwin's Watchmaker*: "Darwinians, by accepting the premise of the argument to design (i.e.,the premise that apparent design must have some historical explanation) have left the door wide open to intelligent design enthusiasts. Darwin's intellectual ancestor is Paley, not Lucretius." (356) Lucretius wrote of the "swerve," and he believed that the random movement of elementary particles was not the mere raw material for a still deterministic Natural Selection; instead, it was the source of true free will; it introduced uncertainty on the human and cosmic scale. [Greenblatt, *The Swerve,* Chapter 8.]

The argument to design supposes that God gave us feet for walking, eyes for seeing, voice for speech. Stripped of its overt theology, it is a mode of thought easily assimilated to a functionalist theory of Natural Selection. But since we can neither enter the mind of God nor have direct and infallible access to the logic of Natural Selection, it is something we can grasp only through hypothetical reverse engineering. Feet are useful for walking: presumably they were selected for that, since creatures with feet were at an advantage in the struggle for existence. But do we appreciate art only because it is useful? Is any trait that isn't useful sure to be eliminated by Natural Selection?

Darwin himself knew better. Even his strongest assertions of Natural Selection have two large caveats: he allows for history and for organic interdependence. "Every detail of structure in every living creature (making some little allowance for the direct action of physical conditions) may be viewed, either as having been of special use to some ancestral form, or as being now of special use to the descendants of this form--either directly, or indirectly through the complex laws of growth." Just how complex those laws of growth are, we shall explore. Evolution can be as indirect as the fiction of Henry James.

Despite its extraordinary beauty and creativity, nature is not a well-oiled machine. Indeed, well-oiled machines are neither beautiful nor creative. It is only by appreciating the specifically organic characteristics of life that we can understand evolution. Only then can evolution become model of creative uncertainty, with important social and political implications, very different from the raw capitalism that led William Jennings Bryan to fear Darwinism.

The Hopeful Monster

My mother was determined that we should see the Amazon during my father's assignment in Brazil, and despite the Embassy's involvement in the impending coup, early in 1964 we flew from Rio to Belem, then took a Catalina sea plane of World War II vintage to Manaus, from which we went by freighter up river to Iquitos. A seven year old boy is inevitably intoxicated by disaster and danger, whether the failure of one of our twin engines on the Catalina – which I, with a window seat, was the first to notice while my father was in conversation with the flight engineer, who had come back to chat with the diplomat – or the anaconda that reputedly was removed from the hold of our freighter the night we sailed from Manaus. With a sense of the credulity of tourists, a teenage boy in Santarem pointed at the river and told us that there was a monster that eats people.

Even today, the tropical rainforest – so well recaptured in David Attenborough's "Jungles" in the BBC *Planet Earth* series – has for me a strange sense of familiarity, tinged with sadness that so much of it is under threat. Its lush diversity is, paradoxically, a hymn to the rigors of natural selection. Just three percent of the Earth's surface holds half its species, because jungles foster competition, interdependence, and specialization.

In the rainforest of Borneo, a pitcher plant lures an ant to drown in its liquid so that it can absorb the nutrients of the ant's decaying body, nutrients it needs because rainforest soil is poor. A red crab spider lives on the pitcher plant's slippery side and fishes up drowning ants, which would be too dangerous to attack otherwise. The spider even has an air-bubble, its own diving bell, so that it can swim to the bottom of the pitcher to fetch mosquito larvae.

The rainforest's food lies mostly in the canopy of its great trees, and because there are no real seasons, there is no one time of flowering or fruiting. Figs are the most reliable of foods. Animals must travel from tree to tree, hence the extraordinary night gliding of the lemur-like colugo, which has skin connecting its legs that acts as a virtual wing – and hence also, no doubt, all the cognitive skills that primates developed from the demands of navigating in trees.

But the reverse engineering method-- of seeing a trait and positing its purpose-- can also be misleading. We see the extraordinary eye spot on a moth wing and surmise that the eye is to frighten potential predators. Yet experiments show that what frightens the predators is *any* bold shape; it need not have been an eye. The apparent mimicry of an eye is in part accidental, a mere function of the process of wing formation, in which pigment radiates from a central point. [Martin Stevens, Cambridge U., *Journal of Behavioural Ecology*.] In the jungle, the fall of a great tree opens up a shaft of light on the otherwise dark forest floor. As David Attenborough says, "the death of a forest giant has to happen" in order for there to be new growth. Yet, of course, the purposeful language of natural theology would be out of place: the tree does not die in order to open new niches; nor is death a trait chosen by natural selection.

We learn even more about nature when we turn from the richness of its near perfection to the embarrassments of its imperfections. The human appendix is not only unnecessary; it is dangerous. Before the age of surgery, you had a twenty percent chance of dying if you got appendicitis. The appendix is a vestige of a useful fermenting pouch in our leaf-eating primate ancestors such as lemurs. lorises, and spider monkeys. Why do we retain it? As Jerry Coyne explains in *Why Evolution Is True*, "selection simply can't shrink the appendix any more without it becoming even more harmful: a smaller appendix may run an even higher risk of being blocked. That might be an evolutionary roadblock to its complete disappearance." Ernst Mayr remarked that "Nothing in biology makes sense except in the light of evolution." Everything that lives today is a transformation of something that came before; every direction life will take must be a development of what is. These transformations can dramatic, but they are also often messy.

Flat fish such as the flounder would be an embarrassment to any engineer. They are now flat, camouflaged bottom dwellers that prey on other fish. But they evolved from normal, symmetrical vertical swimmers, and to get from the ancestral body plan to their present form involves drastic deformations that have to occur during development. They are born as normal, vertical fish of pancake shape with an eye on each side. But once they flip to be side swimmers, the bottom eye would be worse than useless; it would be easily damaged. So during growth it has to migrate over the skull to end on the top side. Evolution requires awkward improvisation; redesign is impossible. This awkwardness is evidence that we are indeed evolutionary creatures, not products of a Biblical Creation or Intelligent Design. It should also be a caution not to assume that a trait is independently "designed" by natural selection.

Without the architect and builder, a house would be a pile of stones. Without the engineer and assembler, a machine would be a jumble of parts. It was in such terms that theologians conceived of Natural Law: a law imposed by God on a universe that otherwise would be chaotic – and they saw chaos only as negative. The Elizabethan theologian Richard Hooker imagines the ruin that would come "if Nature should intermit her course, and leave altogether, though it were but for a while, the observation of her own laws": "The heavenly arch erected over our heads should loosen and dissolve itself…; the times and seasons of the year blend themselves by disordered and confused mixture; the clouds yield no rain; the fruits of the earth pine away, as children at the withered breasts of their mother." [Richard Hooker, *The Laws of Ecclesiastical Polity*, First Book, Section 3, p.78.] It is an uncanny presentiment of climate chaos from global warming. But it is very much not what would happen but for an externally imposed divine law. If we imagine natural selection as the only thing giving order to what otherwise would be total randomness, we remain unwittingly in the paradigm of natural theology and natural law, and it is perhaps the fear that only law, be it divine or Darwinian, separates life from such chaos that makes the battles between fundamentalists and Neo-Darwinians so bitter.

There is an inner logic to living systems which persists even in deformation and monstrosity. Above my desk hangs an etching by Francesco Goya that my father used to call "The Beast Cutting Its Toenails." Notes to the etching say it is actually of three witches, not one monster; the title, "Se Repulen," translates as "They spruce themselves up," and Goya's acid commentary is "This business of having long nails is so pernicious that it is forbidden even in witchcraft." I can see how my father thought of the image as one monster: triangles and trinities have unity and formal perfection. Was the fiercely anti-clerical Goya commenting not only on witches but on the Trinity? But while the three witches look horribly "right," and very much a unity, in nature there are many two-headed monsters but almost no three-headed monsters. In his fascinating and profound article, "The Logic of Monsters," biologist Pere Alberch asks why bicephaly is common but tricephaly virtually nonexistent.

Nature's preference for two-headed monsters over three-headed monsters cannot be genetic. As Alberch notes, "There is no justification at the genetic level to explain the fact that a two-headed morphology is of much more common occurrence than a three-headed one. Since both are maladaptive, and usually lethal, mutations, the effects of selection, can be ruled out as an explanation in this particular case." He adds: "Teratologies [malformations] are often caused by mutations, but the explanation of the resultant patterns of morphological organizationhas to be searched for at the developmental level." A simple duplication causes two-headedness; but for three-headedness you have to fuse a two-headed creature to a one-headed creature – very rare indeed.

Darwinism, Alberch says, is an "externalist" theory of biological organization: you have random variation from genetic mutations, and it is given shape by natural selection. The niche of the well adapted, advantageous function supplies the whole mold for the living form, much as God in Richard Hooker's passage is all that separates the universe from chaos. But teratologies disprove this ultra-functionalist hypothesis, since monsters have form but not survivable function. "The empty spaces, forms that although conceivable are not realized," show that we also need an "internalist" theory, one that looks at structure. Alberch is by no means denying Darwinism; he is arguing for a synthesis. "Order in evolution," he says, "is a combination [of] internally generated order based on the internal dynamics of development, and natural selection, dependent on properties of organism-environment interaction." It is this interaction that makes uncertainty in evolution creative.

"Architecture," observed Goethe, "is frozen music, while music is liquid architecture." The architecture of a living creature is not the work of an Intelligent Designer, nor is it wholly shaped by its utility. Instead it is the frozen music of process, in this case the dynamic processes of development in the growing embryo. Genes affect this process, but it is simplistic and misleading to say they design it or they are a computer program for it. "Teratologies," writes Alberch, "are not only generated in an organized and discrete manner, but they also exhibit generalized transformational rules. These properties are not exclusive to teratologies; rather they are general properties of all developmental systems." The relevant mathematics is not statistics, as in genetics, but one of my high school favorites, transformational geometry, otherwise known as topology. These properties arise through the dynamic processes of embryo growth: chemical diffusion, gravity, even electricity. Changes, including genetic errors, create large scale changes in these processes and thus in the frozen architecture of biological form. We see them, for example, in the duplication that takes the stem that would have been one head and makes it two. But they are equally at work in alterations in development that lead to creative evolutionary advances.

Because organisms are dynamic systems, not inert assemblies of parts, they have a remarkable ability to adjust to errors and perturbations. In his intriguing and compassionate book, *Freaks of Nature*, psychologist and biologist Mark Blumberg discusses our fascination with circus attractions: Tom Thumb, the Bearded Lady, the Elephant Man, the Siamese Twins, who were the staple of P. T. Barnum's circus, just as Kaspar Hauser, the mysterious wild child, was an attraction at a provincial German circus in the dark and haunting film by Werner Herzog. (16) We gape at difference, as we gape at traffic accidents, as a fate we happened to escape. But Blumberg sees more in it. In his book we meet a Dutch goat from 1940 that walks upright on its hind legs, having severe forelimb deformation, and a much more recent dog in Oklahoma City that does likewise; we also meet the wonder Johnny Eck, a real world legless man who acted in the 1932 film *Freaks*. What's remarkable, as Blumberg notes, is not his deformity but his poise. "Eck's movements are so fluid, so natural; yet his condition is the opposite of natural. Like a duck with oversized feet, he bounds over logs, clambers up steps, and balances with impossible grace on a bedpost. He seems perfectly adapted to his condition, and in a sense, he is." (p.106)

In of the most terrifying moments in David Lynch's film *The Elephant Man,* a mob of paying viewers breaks into John Merrick's room in London Hospital. The enlightened Victorian surgeon Frederick Treves had given refuge to Merrick, a man with such severe facial and cranial deformity that he looked somewhat like an elephant. The height of the mob leader's cruelty consists of holding a mirror up to Merrick's deformed face, an image he apparently never had to look at. He screams. Yet we see more. If the Elephant Man's deformed visage mirrors the mob's terrors, the mob mirrors the cruelty in all of us.

It is not the freakish difference from normality that ultimately holds our attention; it is freaks' capacity for adaptation, which reveals our own hidden capabilities. It was Merrick's dignity and intelligence that offered a very different mirror to Treves and other supporters, including Princess Alexandra: the mirror of their own humanity. And this mirror holds true not only psychologically but also in the physiology of development and evolution."Thus, whatever caused the goat to lose its two forelegs – whether genetic mutation or environmental perturbation – the developing system was able to accommodate the change to produce a mobile adult." (p.116) What the two-legged goat ultimately reveals is not freakish at all: "the latent evolutionary potential of developmental systems." The goat did not have a set of genetic instructions for walking on two legs. Rather, during the course of development, it learned to walk despite its abnormality. This tells us something not just about one abnormal specimen but about the course of evolution. Because organisms are not assemblies of parts but are instead developing creatures, all evolutionary change takes place as a reorganization of the developmental process. This reorganization both imposes constraints and opens possibilities that would be extremely unlikely on an à la carte menu of isolated genes and natural selection.

Nowhere is society's fear of the ambiguous more acute than in sexuality. Conservatives condemn homosexuality, transsexuality, and intersexuality as not only abnormal but also "unnatural." Many liberals respond that sexuality is not a personal choice but instead is genetically determined. In *Freaks of Nature,* Blumberg argues that sexual ambiguity is eminently natural, but not because it is written in the genes. He does not believe that it is. "There is," he writes, "a broader dynamic at work, one that captures sexual differentiation in all its forms. This dynamic entails not only the evolutionary construction of development, but the evolutionary construction of *alternative* developments." (250)

Why do men have nipples? Why do women have clitoral rather than vaginal orgasms? As Stephen Jay Gould writes in "Male Nipples and Female Ripples," both sexes are developments of a single body plan. Adaptationists try to explain male nipples and clitoral orgasm as serving a specific function. Actually, however, "males have nipples because females need them." Women experience clitoral orgasm because the clitoris is the evolutionary homologue of the penis. Trying to find a specific evolutionary advantage to male nipples or to clitoral orgasm shows how functionalism blinds us to the fluidity of development and evolution.

This fluidity suggests why it is misguided to attribute homosexuality to the genes. Blumberg asks: "If our gonads are not genetically determined, if our genitalia are not genetically determined, and if our style of play is not genetically determined, then why would we believe that our erotic attractions would be?" (p.217) Blumberg does not mean that sexual orientation is a mere lifestyle choice: epigenetics – the course of development – can be massively committing. But our tendency to see this commitment as a form of genetic determinism "is both unfortunate and false." Liberals' resort to the genetic argument suggests a despairing assumption that only the alibi of genetic determinism can protect same sex couples from prejudice, instead of affirming the worth and dignity of many paths in sexuality, provided that the specific relationships are consensual and caring – of which there is no guarantee in heterosexual relationships either. Sexual ambiguity is one expression of the creativity of all of evolution.

Reductionist biologists love to loathe "hopeful monsters" almost as much as mobs love to loathe freaks. The term "hopeful monster" was coined by German Jewish geneticist Richard Goldschmidt for sudden evolutionary change and became a reviled term in evolutionary theory. Goldschmidt had in mind a macro-mutation: something unlike the very small mutations that bring fine tuning adaptation. Darwin believed that all change was continuous and gradual, a version of the Aristotelian doctrine *Natura non facit saltus* (Nature does not make leaps). And evolutionists assert this gradualist doctrine the more vehemently because creationists cite the poverty of fossil intermediate forms to buttress their assertion that God made each species, perfect and complete. But Goldschmidt and more modern exponents had no use for supernatural explanations. They were simply pointing out that major change is not always just the sum of a lot of small changes over time; some changes have leverage. That is because the organism is a developmental system, and changes early in development have a much bigger effect than fine tuning changes as the embryo matures. But of course most random changes are deleterious, and it seemed to many biologists that a change early in development, having many effects, would almost be bound to be fatal. We shall look more at this in the following section. But in the two-legged goat and Johnny Eck, we already have a clue. Developing systems are adaptive and creative. Monsters are not in themselves Goldschmidt's "hopeful monster," but, as Stephen Jay Gould said, they are "helpful" in suggesting the potential for large scale biological reorganization.

Creative Constraints

Americans who have asked for directions in England will never forget the inveterate English response: twists and turns from High Street to a bewildering series of lanes, followed by the cheerful "You can't (cahn't) miss it." Visitors to Maine proverbially get a different response: "You can't get there (they-ahh) from here (hee-ahh)." I felt it keenly driving in the dark in a rental car the night of my cousin's wedding rehearsal dinner, on the circuitous and ill marked roads of Southport Isle, till a policeman stopped me and gave me a breath test.

Evolution faces something of the same problem as the hapless tourist. Nothing will come of nothing; everything requires a point of departure and a way to get there. This is the difference between biology and engineering: the engineer wipes the slate clean, comes up with a new design, has the parts machine tooled and assembled. As Francois Jacob points out in *The Possible and the Actual,* "The electric light bulb does not derive from the candle nor does the jet engine derive from the internal combustion engine." Evolution depends on transformation and involves "solutions that a reasonable God would have never used."

Some paintings of The Annunciation, such as a famous one by Fra Angelico, feature the angel with his arms folded modestly before Mary, who in turn has her arms folded modestly before the angel. In other depictions, such as one by Annibale Carracci, the angel gestures dramatically. But in a scene representing a biological impossibility, namely virgin birth, the artists hardly troubled themselves with the essential impossibility of angels: to have wings, they would presumably first have to disarm. Just as the flounder must reorganize, however awkwardly, to be a side swimmer, angels would have to make wings out of the arm stems. And this leaves you wondering how intelligent angels would be, since so much of the brain co-evolves with the hand. There are other problems such as weight (leading to the quip that angels take themselves lightly). Mammalian fliers are more likely to be the size of bats. Meanwhile, we have transferred our dreams of hovering omniscience from angels to drones. "The dreams of reason," as Goya observed, "bring forth monsters."

But if constraints explain why angels can't fly, they also help explain why birds can.

The Archer and the Tree

Who does not love to look at the night sky, to peer at stars, those points of light at the ends of space? For many, the stars are the opening to infinity. Or is it infinities? The night sky is a congress of times, as we see each star not in an instantaneous present, but in its past, depending on how far away it is and thus how long its light took to reach us. And since stars are different distances, each of these points of light represents a different time.

As night reveals the stars, winter exposes the structure of branches. Surely one of the fascinations of trees is their ramification of possibilities. They are, in José Borges' famous phrase, gardens of forking paths, signifying to us the divergent possibilities of roads not traveled. And as the night sky is a congress of times, the tree is a congress of outcomes. It is endlessly intriguing to think of all of these existing, just as the whole tree exists. Yet I think that reality exceeds the mystery of our metaphors and the seduction of labyrinths. I am not a believer in many worlds or multiverses, and even if they did exist, we would have no access to them. The entanglement of the quantum world is hypnotic, but in our world, the limitation of choice, which we experience, is also the basis of freedom and responsibility. The growing complexity of evolution occurs not despite but because of limitation, which eliminates options only to open new ones at a higher level. Constraint becomes creativity.

The tree gives us a better metaphor than William Pailey's watchmaker, or Richard Dawkins' blind watchmaker, with which to understand the limits and the glories of evolution. The tortuous course of one branch is chaotic, but together the branches make the order of the tree's crown. Any one of these branches is but a token of the order embedded in the type, but there is no straight and ideal branch.

Having devoted a chapter to assailing the myth of design, we will refrain from saying that life is designed for a world of creative uncertainty. What we can say is that somehow, life, with its wetness, its vulnerabilities, and its fleshy imperfections, is a system with an exquisite affinity for Creative Uncertainty. The embodied creativity of life is stretched out in the tapestry of evolution, and it is to this vulnerable yet resilient model that we can turn for embodied wisdom now that the hubris of Homo Sapiens has put the biosphere at risk.

7 Reinventing Philosophy

At one point in the development of this book, my father and I took scissors to the manuscript and laid the scraps, sentence by sentence, on the living room sofa. Then we assembled it in reverse order. One version went from the Big Bang at the beginning of the universe to another kind of bang – the risk of nuclear war. The other version began with that risk and worked its way back to the origin of the universe. Unfortunately, neither version persuaded early readers that cosmology had anything to do with politics.

In our attempt to be relevant and practical, my father and I missed the essential middle term: philosophy. We forgot that we were in search not just of correct answers (which our political allies were sure they already knew) but of appropriate questions, ways of approaching not just the immediate circumstances of 1980 but the much larger dilemmas that are still with us, only much more acutely, in the third decade of the new Millennium.

Most disciplines seek answers; philosophy seeks questions. When you ask questions about the questions, you are doing philosophy. Educators call this process finding "essential questions." John McTighe says an "essential question"

- Is open ended; that is, it typically will not have a single, final, and correct answer;
- Is thought provoking and intellectually engaging, often sparking discussion and debate;
- Calls for higher-order thinking, such as analysis, inference, evaluation, prediction. It cannot be effectively answered by recall alone;
- Points toward important, transferable ideas within (and sometimes across) disciplines.

Essential questions are an invitation to philosophy, which is never more important than when we are facing an existential crisis, one that cannot be solved by technical fixes but requires us to ask ourselves how and why we want to live.

Socrates famously claimed that the unexamined life was not worth living. His essential questions --- in the form of dialogues exposing how much less his protagonists knew than they thought they knew, earned him a death sentence at the hands of the Athenian state. Today, authorities do not bother to put philosophers to death. The Establishment prefers to dismiss philosophy as ridiculous than to dignify it as dangerous. If all else fails, it can finally be accepted as true but boring. Anxious parents steer their children to more remunerative majors, while professors argue that it is a good preparation for law or business school.

But the blame for philosophy's marginal status lies not only with society's materialism. It also lies with philosophy itself. It is hard to make a better case for philosophy than philosophers themselves make for it. Academic philosophy is a corpus, a field of study with sub-departments each with specialized terminology that outsiders struggle to understand; but it is also a corpse, something whose own practitioners no longer believe in. Reputable academic philosophers tell students that studying philosophy will teach them to think more clearly and consistently, but they rarely claim that philosophy is key to saving the world. Such a claim would be met with a nervous titter as the sign of a well-meaning but naive newcomer.

But such a response is not in fact sophisticated. Philosophy could help save society, but only once it saves itself from the errors into which it itself has fallen.

The problem goes all the way back to the construction of reason in Western thought. Philosophy means, literally, the love of wisdom. Yet wisdom is as foreign to our culture as philosophy is marginal.

What is the wisdom we have lost in knowledge?
What is the knowledge we have lost in information?

In its first, cosmological phase in Ionia, on the west coast of what is now Turkey, the First Philosophers sought a new understanding of nature and human nature, one based upon theory rather than myth. Rather than explain the world as the work, or play, of somewhat capricious anthropomorphic gods (or, later, in the three Axial religions, of one anthropomorphic god), these philosophers asked what the world is made of – Air, Earth, Water, or Fire. But really, this was a debate not about a physical substance but about a fundamental natural law. Do we live in a world of matter (earth) or process (fire)?

The philosopher Simon Critchley in his fascinating lecture "Philosophy's Tragedy" argues that philosophy made a fatal mistake right at its foundation in excluding story for theory. He examines the extraordinary wisdom of the Oedipus story – that of a man blinded by his brilliance and arrogance, who commits incest, sees his kingdom suffer, and leads an investigation that points back to him. Oedipus, Critchley notes, means "I know."

Theory is essentially static: in our conscious mind, we construct a geometric model of the apparently changing world around us. The visual mind cannot see time. By contrast, the world of stories, of dreams, of myth, is inherently temporal – full of change, of surprise, of novelty. Things just happen, unchallengeable because they are first person experiences in which we have no choice but to be involved. But intellectual experiences are based on skepticism: staring at a structure, looking in from the outside. Nothing happens. Time has been extracted.

But one of these pre-Socratic philosophers tried to escape that trap. Heraclitus saw change and structure as inseparable. His most famous maxim is "You can never step in the same river twice," or, more accurately, "In the same river, ever different waters flow. Here is an extraordinary insight that prefigures 20th Century biologist Ludwig von Bertalanffy's Open System: a pattern maintaining itself in a flow of matter and energy, structure that feeds upon process. Static things are degraded by time;

dynamic systems feed upon time for self-maintenance, self-repair, and (with life) for reproduction.

But Heraclitus lost this debate at the outset of Western philosophy. The winner was Parmenides, who argued that time is an illusion. How can anything change? A thing, by definition, must be itself. If it changes, it becomes different from itself. Therefore it is no longer its old self. So nothing really changes. *Quod erat demonstrandum*. Substance metaphysics is not kind to chameleons or caterpillars, or indeed to any living thing.

The separation of the structure from the process is the opening gambit of Western philosophy and leads to almost all its tortured positions over history. As Alfred North Whitehead writes in *Process and Reality*, "The vicious separation of the flux from the permanence leads to the concept of an entirely static God, with eminent reality, in relation to an entirely fluent world, with deficient reality. But if the opposites, static and fluent, have once been so explained as separately to characterize diverse actualities, the interplay between the thing which is static and the things which are fluent involves contradiction at every step in its explanation. Such philosophies include the notion of illusion as a fundamental principle – the notion of 'mere appearance.' This is the final Platonic problem."

When reality as we experience it is an illusion, then truth belongs to a select few: the philosopher kings of Plato's *Republic*.

Democritus tried to reconcile change and stasis, and made an enormously influential move to do so. He posited atoms – small unchanging building blocks; only their arrangement changed. In this notion lies the origin of the reductionist method. Break a complex thing into its unchanging elements; then observe how forces act upon those things to produce apparent change.

The next, enormously influential step occurred at the beginning of the early modern period with Galileo and Newton. By studying the motion of a ball rolling down an inclined plane, Galileo realized that what we perceive as motion was really just inertia: if you filter out friction, the ball really just continues blindly doing what it was already doing. Motion is arbitrary, really a form stasis, like a car coasting. What matters is not change but acceleration. And this, Newton posited, was the result of force acting on an inert mass. The world had been entirely mechanized into forces and masses, all known and predictable. Such a world appeared radically different from the static, ancient and medieval world – yet was fundamentally the same. It had incorporated motion and thus the ability to change the word. Yet by reducing motion to inertia, to something passive acted upon by forces that could be expressed in mathematical equations, it gave us the mechanistic, deterministic world picture. It was a world we could predict and control. It was also a world in which we were both almighty and abject, the hidden God, the puppet and puppeteer, the inert mass of atoms acted upon by hidden forces, and yet the calculating intelligence that can solve mathematical equations and predict (and manipulate) the action of everything – or everyone – else. Such powers became truly demonic in the 19th Century, when joined with the motive power of fire.

Until the professionalization of academia in the 19th Century, there was no fixed demarcation between science, economics, theology, and philosophy. René Descartes was one of the greatest and most influential mathematicians and philosophers. A Cartesian diagram, with horizontal and vertical coordinates, can plot the values of an equation over time, as in a parabolic curve, which describes the height of a ball you throw into the air as it reaches its apex and again falls. The result is that you see a temporal process as a spatial, essentially timeless shape: time reduced to space.

Descartes was famous for his dualism between mind and matter – or mind and body. Insofar as we are bodies, or animals, we are mere machines: our freedom and humanity consists solely in our consciousness and free will, which are immaterial. The irony is that this dualism leads to intractable dilemmas when you consider both computers and brains. A computer fits the Cartesian model: the hardware, the silicon chips, are the machine; the software, the computer program, is the mind, which the physical computer executes. There is no room for freedom in such a dualism. Both its so-called mind and body are mechanistic. The more we understand about biological mind, be it in humans or animals, the more we understand that it is embedded in, and inseparable from, our bodies. Our freedom comes not despite, but because of, our corporeality.

[continued]

Reinventing Philosophy (Part Two)

The world is made up of stories, not of atoms, says the American poet Muriel Rukeyser in her collection *The Speed of Darkness.* Human reason has long appealed to the image of timeless enlightenment and even, in some of its greatest exponents – from Parmenides and Plato to Albert Einstein – to timelessness as an absolute principle. But the great navigators of darkness – the bats who inhabit caves – rely on time for their powers of echo-location. The great Enlightenment project – the quest for pure reason, corrupted by the quest for absolute power – has failed, and the West has taken life, including the human species, to the brink of extinction. Can we embrace the Endarkenment as a new Enlightenment? Can we lead humanity to the cave where the human mind itself was formed?

The most famous passage in Western philosophy is the allegory of the cave in Plato's *Republic.* Socrates describes ordinary mortals held prisoners in a cave mistaking the flickering images on the wall, which are but dancing shadows, for reality itself.

These images are cast by puppets illuminated from behind by a fire. The prisoners have never seen real objects, only shadows which they mistake for reality. The philosopher leads the prisoners out of the cave to the brilliant light of the sun, where they at last see reality itself: perfect, unchanging forms. Oh, and in this ideal republic, there will be no art or poetry or drama – no illusion, only reality. It will be a world of absolute reason. Indeed, many commentators think the well governed (and totalitarian) Republic is chiefly a metaphor for a well governed mind. But what does that say about Plato's idea of a well governed mind?

I have always found the allegory of the Cave very puzzling. Where did Plato get such an elaborate image of shadows cast on the wall of a cave as illusion, imitation, or mere appearance in contrast with the absolute reality to which the philosopher of absolute reason has privileged access? Could it be that rather than a mere allegory, Plato is giving us a mythic version of actual history as invading Iron Age Greeks encountered earlier Europeans who had been cave dwellers during the Ice Age?

Flickering images on the walls of caves were not idle illusions but transformative experiences in the formation of the human mind. For Ice Age peoples, caves were essential shelters, geothermal shelters from the bitter cold of the surface. But entering a cave and crawling in darkness from one chamber to another of a cave is a terrifying, indeed hallucinatory experience. Paleontologists now believe the extraordinary cave paintings of animals and anthropomorphic hybrids that Paleolithic peoples portrayed on cave walls were part of rituals which enacted and helped bring about the birth of the modern human mind.

According to Stephen Mithen in *The Prehistory of the Mind* and David Lewis Williams in *The Mind in the Cave,* about 100,000 years ago, hominids grew in brain size to something that would support what we know as human intelligence. But that did not at once lead to modern human intelligence. First, a rather primitive general intelligence split into separate, specialized divisions, each of which greatly developed. Then the divisions were reconnected, like a cave with chambers and passageways between them. On the walls of the cave they painted stunningly lifelike images of the animals they hunted, and they celebrated the hunt in rituals in the terrifying darkness of the cave. Hallucinatory experience, art, and social cohesion were of imagination all compact.

How extraordinary, then, of Plato to reject this primal bonding of humanity in his manifesto for the primacy of philosophy, a science drenched in the light of pure reason, able to grasp things in themselves rather than flickering, ever-moving images of them.

Why do I dwell on this piece of ancient history? Actually, there is no ancient history. The explosively accelerating pace of history to which we have become almost accustomed leads us to forget that all history is as yesterday. The human mind, synthesized fifty thousand years ago, is very young and very unstable. Art, religion, and philosophy are not luxuries: they are the practices which permit humans to be humans, and in which we rehearse and negotiate our relation to the ecosystem, whose existence we now threaten.

Plato dismissed direct human experience in all its sensuous ambiguity as flickering images on the wall of a cave – illusion. Only theoretical knowledge based on timeless ideas or forms was real to him. Art he dismissed as tertiary: images based on images.

In the words of the great French philosopher Henri Bergson, the Western mind adopted the analytic and spatial at the expense of the emergent and temporal. It thereby excluded uncertainty and therefore creativity right from its foundational documents, banishing the tantalizing alternative offered by 6th Century BCE Ionian philosopher Heraclitus, who saw that the same river flows with ever different waters. In other words, in an active system, structure and process are one. Instead, Plato turned to the other school of pre-Socratic philosophers, the time-denying ones influenced by Parmenides and Pythagoras, who discovered significant mathematical relationships in space that were valuable in architecture. Yet, as Goethe remarked, architecture is frozen music.

As Will Hunt notes in his book *Underground,* being in a cave disables the hippocampus and produces a unique feeling of disorientation. Disorientation – what John Keats calls "Negative Capability -- that is when man is capable of being in uncertainties, Mysteries, doubts, without any irritable reaching after fact & reason" – can be a gateway for creativity. No wonder that the early modern Homo sapiens found in caves more than shelter from the cold of Ice Age Europe; they found terrain to invent art and religion, indeed to invent the human mind as a creative fusion of multiple intelligences. And no wonder that Plato, scornfully rejecting the frenzied rites of earlier peoples, also rejected the creative uncertainty of time in favor of the timeless stability of mathematical idealization. The Republic is also an ode to totalitarianism – though scholars suggest that Plato's ideal republic is a metaphor for the mind. In that case, Plato is not so much calling for authoritarian governance of an actual republic as for rigid control of the mind. For centuries, they have gone together.

We would seem in better luck with Aristotle, who was an observant biologist and a forerunner of Darwin. Nothing is to be gained from reducing a complex story to caricature. Still – and critically for the whole history of Western thought – you can observe the limits of Aristotle's comprehension of change in his notion of hylomorphism. Aristotle believed that an embryo was a miniature of an adult, like a microfilm image: much smaller but already possessing the complete form. In other words, he overlooked the process of differentiation which is at the heart of biological development. He also believed that form came entirely from the male, with the female merely providing the medium for growth.

The great weakness of Western thought in contrast with Asian doctrines has been the West's fear of indeterminacy. (It is, however, a form of inverted Eurocentrism to suppose that all other human thought is the opposite. It isn't. Taoism celebrates the indeterminate, as does Sufism, but much Indian philosophy is as logically rigorous as anything in the West and may indeed have inspired much of it.)

Philosophy is often defined as an attempt to answer the deepest questions (such as "Does God exist?" "Do we have free will?" "Is there anything after death?") based on unaided reason. That is, if you go into a cave, or out on the desert, or you fast for days, or take hallucinogens, and then you see God, that does not count as strictly philosophical knowledge. But also, in traditional philosophical terms, it is not a philosophical answer if you rely upon contingent facts; you are supposed to be able to reason it -- but with unaided, pure reason (if not mathematical logic).

Reinventing Philosophy
Part Three

In his famous three Critiques – *The Critique of Pure Reason, The Critique of Practical Reason,* and *The Critique of Judgement,* Immanuel Kant asks three questions: "What can I know?", "What should I do?", and "What may I hope for?" They are still the central questions for any human being, even though their specific content in the 21st Century has changed vastly since Kant's day in the late 18th Century

The changes in the following three centuries concern both the sense in relation to which we gauge scientific questions and the content of Kant's hopes versus ours, as he was still thinking in religious – that is, theistic – terms. So Kant had to wrestle with antimonies between a mechanistic science and a mechanistic God, what A. N. Whitehead calls the "monstrous twin issue of limited metaphysic and clear logical intellect." Kant wanted to know things that today we realize are chimerical, ill-formed questions: God, the purpose of the universe, the immortality of the soul, are not so much illusions to be exterminated with the disinfectant of scientific materialism (as Whitehead quipped of Voltaire's atheism), as they are "fallacies of misplaced concreteness" (another

Whitehead phrase): literal, anthropomorphic formulations that we want, but would find very disappointing, in their Christmas wrapping.

What we have today is not mere uncertainty about those old, misshapen hopes; instead, it is a much tougher, more rooted uncertainty, an uncertainty of being rather than of mere knowing, a set of challenges at once theoretical and practical, at once scientific, moral, aesthetic, and, if you will, religious, about how to maintain the resilience of life at a time when life as a whole is critically threatened.

The human mind, as we saw in the previous section, is an astonishingly recent achievement – connected only yesterday – 50,000 years ago – at the same time as humans in Europe took refuge from the Ice Age by sheltering in caves and there found an objective correlative for the mind in the cave itself, creating there the unique human practices we know as art and religion. An order of magnitude more recently, Plato promised to lead us out of the flickering images of imagination into the brilliant sunshine of pure reason, where philosopher kings would show them the absolute truth of Ideas themselves – an example of the West's idolatry of narrow rationality.

Kant's Critiques recognized that such absolute certainty is unattainable. We have no direct access to the *Ding an sich*, the *thing in itself*, absolute, unchallenged Truth. As Kant believed, we formulate our conceptions, be they scientific, philosophical, or religious, only in our familiar terms of time and space. And while these terms work extremely well for physical reality, they work extremely badly for metaphysical reality. That is how Kant explains what 20th Century physicist Eugene Wigner calls "the unreasonable effectiveness of mathematics." Why should nature be law-like, and why should we be able to predict and manipulate it? But equally: why, beyond certain limits, should we be unable to do so?

This question looked very different in Kant's day than it does in our own. To Kant, it was the difference between the material, mechanical on the one hand and the spiritual on the other. Yet French philosopher Henri Bergson pointed out at the turn of the 20th Century that classical dualism put the boundary in the wrong place. The problem with the mechanistic concept of nature was not that it was confined to space and time, but on the contrary, that it was confined to spatialized time. A "time" that you could see as if it were an object, a "time" from which uncertainty has been extracted, a "time" without surprise or novelty, is not time at all. This world, the world of inertia and momentum, is the world of Galileo and Newton. It does not deserve the category of "Pure Reason."

If we stop looking for inert things and start looking for interconnected, open systems, then the wall between a material world and an ineffable world of ideas will tumble down, and a world of patterns, of processes in time, will appear. Why attempt to reconstruct philosophy? Because it is a very bad idea to have intellectual tools that are antithetical to the living, breathing world we inhabit. It is an especially bad idea if you live in a world in crisis and yours is a culture in a hurry. Even or especially if your intentions are good, you are likely to destroy the village in order to save it.

- What can I know?
- What should I do?
- What may I hope?

Today, it is again possible to address Kant's questions in a fresh and meaningful way. Kant said that for him there were two objects of wonder: the starry sky at night and the moral law in his heart. Kant was a distinguished astronomer, so in addition to the awe he felt, he also saw a sky ruled by the inexorable, mechanical laws of Newton. Of this universe, the French microbiologist Jacques Monod says: "Now at last does he waken at the end of his millenary dream to find himself wandering on the edge of an alien world, a world that is deaf to his music, just as indifferent to his hopes at it is to his suffering or his crimes." The astrophysicist

Stephen Weinberg agrees: "The more the world seems comprehensible," he writes, "the more it also seems pointless."

Is this the world we see? First, consider Jacques Monod's statement that the world is deaf to our music, just as indifferent to our hopes as to our suffering or our crimes. Can the universe be deaf? Not any more than it can hear. You can be as deaf as a stone, but a stone cannot be deaf. Deafness is meaningful as the absence of hearing – when that is possible. What if the universe hears – through us? Can the universe be "indifferent" except as a projection of our own failure to care and of the pain that brings us? The intense anti-romanticism is not realism but inverted romanticism. That would be true even if physical understanding were still where it was in the days of Newton and Kant.

But, of course, it isn't, and what we have learned in 20th and 21st Century physics gives us new reason to see humanity "at home in the universe," in the words of Stuart Kauffman – not at the center of the universe (it has none, and that concept would be meaningless if it did). David Lewis-Williams, whose analysis of caves we drew on for insight on the origins of the human mind, has a subsequent book on the Neolithic. These first settled civilizations had a tremendous impulse for architecture – vast stone structures that for them recreated the universe. And for us? In what world do we live? It is one in which we are ironically marginal; yet the reality of our wounded planet is equally marginal to us, as we are incapable of curbing our gluttony and violence as the ecosystem nears the breaking point.

By the end of the 19th Century, there was a general feeling that Western philosophy was finished. After Maxwell in physics and Darwin in biology, there remained mopping up but no great conceptual revolution seemed possible. Those, of course, were famous last words on the eve of revolutions (in science as well as the streets) that mark the Twentieth Century.

The first half of the 20th Century saw three efforts. None of them gained outright acceptance in Anglo-American philosophy, which was in the grip of the convulsion to abolish speculative philosophy almost altogether, which began in modernist Turn of the Century Vienna and then captured the English-speaking world, which found anti-philosophical philosophy almost as satisfying as extreme free market economics.

What Bergson, Heidegger, and Whitehead had in common – unlike their modernist contemporaries such as Einstein and Wittgenstein -- was an embrace of time and therefore of uncertainty. I have earlier quoted Stephen Toulmin suggesting that the political and religious chaos of the 17th Century led René Descartes and others to seek mathematical certainty, in contrast to Montaigne's very different skepticism, which was comfortable in uncertainty. I believe the same was true of Einstein and Wittgenstein, for all their apparent radicalism; and I believe the embrace of uncertainty is what makes Bergson, Heidegger, and Whitehead ultimately far more radical.

In Henri Bergson, this arises as an aesthetic revolt against the positivism of the late 19th Century. I had never thought of it in this way, but in a famous 1956 article, art critic George Heard Hamilton notes that the essence of Impressionist painting is that it is the artistic embodiment of the positivist philosophy of August Comte. Claude Monet's "Cathedrals" consists of dots, for example, just as if you examined a color photograph with a magnifying glass. Together, these dots tell you not only your exact location in space but also your exact point in time: just how the light was dappling upon each point at one thousandth of a second when the photographer clicked the shutter. But here's the catch: "Cathedrals" is not a photograph; it's a painting, which surely took Monet many hours to paint. He had to construct an artificial instant and hold it painstakingly in his head to deposit all the dots on the canvas; it was never what he actually saw. The result was to remove the dialogue between viewer and canvas. Monet's "Cathedrals" leaves nothing to the viewer: it tells her not only exactly where she is but also exactly when, at that one isolated instant. (It has often been noted that if Western culture had not pursued this strange way of seeing, photographs would not look natural to us.)

In Newtonian mathematics, time is paradoxically timeless. The differential calculus depends on a brilliant abstraction: the infinitesimal. An object that is accelerating has a speed that is getting bigger (that's what acceleration is, constantly increasing speed). So what speed is this object (say, a rocket) going exactly three seconds after it is launched, as it accelerates? In some sense it is a meaningless question, because acceleration is constantly changing speed, so it is never going just 300 miles per hour. It was going 290 miles per hour, and the next time you checked, it is going 310 miles per hour. But if we pretend that there is such a thing as an *instant,* then yes, at that instant it might have been going 300 miles per hour. It's a strange intellectual construct, because, if the interval were truly of zero time, it could travel zero distance, so it could have zero speed. So Newton and his arch-enemy Leibniz invented the so-called differential, or the infinitesimal: an interval of time which is more than nothing but less than anything. In other words, a point in time is an abstraction from lived reality. And that is the abstraction that the points of a French Impressionist painting such as Monet's "Cathedrals" embody in an artistic equivalent of the concept of the instant. In the late 19th Century, it seemed the last word in modernity.

Twentieth Century physics, however, realized that matter was not made up of hard, tiny particles but also (in an equally valid description) of waves which have a "tendency to exist" over a duration.

As a philosopher, Henri Bergson was very close to artists – not only Paul Cézanne in painting but also Marcel Proust and Virginia Woolf in literature. For them, the present time was not a "point" (as in the cliché, "at this point in time") but wave connecting past and future. As Bergson writes in *Creative Evolution,* "It is only our habitual confusion of time with space, and the assimilation of time with space, that makes us think the whole is given, if only in the eyes of God." Cézanne's masterpiece, Mont-Saint Victoire, is painted as an organic, enduring presence, not an object caught at an instant, expressing a very different view of time from Monet's "Cathedrals."

It is no wonder that Bergson's first book, *Essai sur les donnés immédiates de la conscience (Essay on the Immediate Givens of Consciousness),* is translated into English as *Time and Free Will,* or that his most prominent early admirer was the greatest American philosopher, William James.

For a philosopher of change, life is the ultimate subject, and evolutionary theory is the ultimate proving ground. To the two theories that dominated his own time and, far more disgracefully, take up most of the intellectual bandwidth even today – mechanical causality and Intelligent Design – Bergson says, "a curse on both your Houses!" (He uses the term "finalism" to mean that the result is set from the beginning, so that the outcome is planned. In the debate about evolution, it is the position of the fundamentalists, who argue that order can emerge only if it is God's plan.) As he puts it early in *Creative Evolution:*

"The doctrine of finalism (that is, Intelligent Design) in its extreme form such as we find in Leibniz for example, implies that things and beings only realize [carry out] a program that had already been set. But if there is nothing unforeseen, if there is no invention or creation in the universe, then time becomes useless. As in the mechanistic hypothesis, one supposes here that everything is settled once and for all." And the life-work of Henri Bergson is to reject determinism and move beyond it.

This is what he attempts in *Creative Evolution.* This is the book that got him in a great deal of trouble and still has him referred to in scornful, condescending terms in the Anglo-Saxon intellectual world. We are sure who his friends are, and as well as *Creative Evolution,* they will have a Bible and a check from the Heartland Institute [fundamentalist anti-Darwinists] in their briefcase. And Bergson, poor man, is dead and can't say what he thinks of them.

So what does Bergson mean when he calls evolution "creative"? What exactly is the "élan vital"? Perhaps he did not quite know. But he planted an idea which can be clarified using 21st Century biology as a template for a creative philosophy for our time.

Alfred North Whitehead, on the other hand, was a mathematician, and early in his career the closest collaborator of Bertrand Russell. The irony, though, was that Russell was a political radical (if a great aristocrat) yet an intellectual conservative in the sense of mechanist, while Whitehead, who came with the starchy innocence of the country parsonage, and loyally sent his son to die in the First World War (to which Russell fiercely objected), yes, Whitehead was the intellectual radical of the two. But first, together, they completed a grand common project, only to have a clever young man devise a counter-proof.

The effort was to derive all of mathematics from logic, to realize, finally, the dream of Pythagoras, Parmenides, and Plato, to establish a final and certain Truth. Logic, Gregory Bateson noted, consists of "If… then" sentences, but there is only logic – and no time – in those "then"s.

Austrian mathematical logician Kurt Gödel thought up the evil magic sentence that, as in a fairy tale, brought down the castle. It is an advanced variant of the old sentence "I am telling a lie." If you are telling the truth, then the sentence must be true, which, when you unpack it, means you must be telling a lie. But if you are telling a lie, then the sentence must be true, which means it must be true that you are telling a lie. In short, either way, it yields a contradiction. This is the trap that comes from so-called self-referential sentences. I can talk about anything else, and my sentence is true or false. But if my sentence refers to that very sentence, then if the sentence says it is false, it generates a contradiction.

Gödel's variant says "This sentence is unprovable." If the sentence is provable, then it's false. If, on the other hand, the sentence is true, then there must be at least one unprovable sentence, namely that one. Therefore, for any formal logical system, the system must be incomplete.

What Gregory Bateson pointed out is that logic twists itself into such knots because it pretends to be about timeless truth, whereas in fact every sentence is an action that changes the world. So what you have is not a contradiction; instead, you have a new situation. Not even logic describes a static state of affairs, because every sentence changes the world it describes. This may be clearer if we discuss ordinary language rather than formal logic. If someone says "I love you," they may change or at least awaken the other person's love (or, sometimes, revulsion). It is not a neutral descriptive statement; it's an action. Language, like all life, exists in time, and time brings surprise and change.

I do not know whether it was the impact of Gödel's proof shattering Whitehead and Russell's glass palace of the *Principia Mathematica,* but Whitehead and Russell parted intellectual ways. More likely, it was Russell's conviction that to be an effective activist, especially in fighting for atheism, he had to be as simple and clear as possible, versus Whitehead's interest in the paradoxical findings of physics of the early 20th Century. At any rate, Russell was a reductionist, Whitehead an exponent (an English-language Bergson) of what he calls "the philosophy of organism."

War-shocked intellectuals of the '20s once again wondered whether these strange intellectual findings from physics did not point to quite a different intellectual world than a side of beef, a pint of ale, and shares in the railways. The Great War certainly did. But there were divergent reactions: toward new certainties; toward nihilism and deconstruction of all metaphysics; and finally toward a new metaphysics based on the organic.

And so, past mid-life, Whitehead began giving book-length lecture series of endowed lectures – ultimately and most magnificently, *Process and Reality,* which had been the Gifford Lectures at the University of Edinburgh in 1929.

Whitehead did what only a mathematician with a specialization in logic could have done. He offered a complete metaphysical system based on process rather than upon substance. To do this, he created an entire terminology, making it formidably inaccessible. If you use good plain English and say "Things change," you are still starting with good British "things" and then making them briskly do something – in this case, change. The point is that what we perceive as things (substances, in the terminology of traditional "substance metaphysics" are themselves processes that appear stable because of flow, not despite it. The boulder in a stream is a conservative structure (a rock) withstanding flow, but the stream itself is a dynamic structure interdependent with flow.

Whitehead therefore names the "atom," that is, the least unit, of his system an "Actual Occasion." In a dialectical relationship to this, he posits "Eternal Objects," which are to Whiteheadian philosophy what Universals are to Western philosophy, properties of which specifics partake. [Every circle partakes of circularity, for example. Circularity is the universal, while every specific circle we see is just an approximation to it, in the Platonic model.] Whitehead is able to escape the subjectivity which haunts Western philosophy. As he says: "For Kant, the world emerges from the subject; for the philosophy of organism, the subject emerges from the world." (106)

Every Actual Occasion has two aspects, as a Subject and as a Superject. The novelist-polymath Arthur Koestler put this differently by saying the fundamental biological entity is a Janus-faced Holon, a whole to its parts and a part to a larger whole.

But does this mean that we are only showing our parochialism in preferring our own level – that of organisms, over the microcosmos inside us or the ecosystem to which we belong? Gaia theory treats the ecosystem as itself being a living organism.

Here I will show myself as unfashionably individualistic. I think organisms are unique and are significantly different from the living systems they contain (the micro-cosmos, the biota that inhabit us) and the living systems to which they belong (the eco-system). Obliterating these differences can also hide our unique responsibilities. Consciousness is a special feature of death and sex, of beings that know they will die and have to make painful choices; in short, of our way of being-in-the-world.

Ultimately, Whitehead's attempt to construct a system goes further than I would wish to. He is right that we do not see things except in terms of categories. But is it necessary to construct algebra of abstract categories, using psychological terms such as "enjoy" when one system incorporates another but no taking of afternoon tea is involved?

An alternative is poetry's reliance on metaphor, with constant awareness of its limitation. It is a philosophy of the concrete, though only provisional. As Gregory Bateson says, each act of vision is dual: you can look at it, or you can look with it. You can use it as a way of seeing, as a model.

Bridging some of these differences is 20th Century science, used philosophically – that is, in quest of models but also with critical awareness of their limitations. The latter is one reason I am least enthusiastic about using Quantum physics as a source of mystical insight, and most enthusiastic about Evo-Devo, the intersection of Evolutionary and Developmental biology as a source of models for practical wisdom and illumination of creativity on many levels.

But before turning to those lessons, I want to discuss another philosopher, and the only one who has received the compliment of being called a "dangerous mind," and for good reason: Martin Heidegger.

Like Henri Bergson, Heidegger was eager to liberate time from Cartesian space, the mere *Res Extensa* of mechanical clock time. But he was even more eager to prove that his French predecessor had failed to do so. He maintained that Bergson's *durée* (a mass of lived or endured time) lacked the ecstatic moments that are the basis of transformation. In his book The Origin of Time, comparing Bergson and Heidegger, American philosopher Heath Massey finds that Bergson, not Heidegger, is the more original,and that Bergson's slow, thick has more ground for true originality than Heidegger's bolts of lightning.

This raises the question whether there is a connection between Heidegger's thought and his membership in the Nazi Party. Heidegger accepted the position as Rector of the University of Freiburg in 1933 and his infamous address in praise of fascism.

But Heidegger does not reduce to a bill of indictment, and he has some extraordinary insights. He is a highly verbal thinker, and many of his observations turn on word-play in German. One is between "Sein" and "Seind," which both translate into English "Being." But "Sein" means something like "the ground of Being," "the wellsprings of your existence," while "Seind" means "happening to exist." For the more important Being, Heidegger also uses "Dasein," "Being There," our existential experience of being "thrown" into the world. At the same time, we slip into a similar confusion: We confuse "Being" with "Beings," and thus think there must be a "Supreme Being," rather than honoring the indeterminate ground of all Being.

Of all the people who could have discarded Heidegger, Hannah Arendt had that right, and she refused to do so. As his former lover, muse, student-teacher, she remained loyal – though critical – in the years of his disgrace. In Anglo-American philosophy departments, Heidegger's dalliance with fascism became another excuse to reduce philosophy to dry word games in Analytic Philosophy and abandon the larger questions of existence. Meanwhile, however, Continental philosophy – including Levinas, Sartre, Merleau-Ponty, and de Beauvoir – owed him a great debt.

Arendt's interests were different from the Existentialists.' Arendt was interested in practices that would preserve society from totalitarianism of the right or the left. Thus she wanted to offer a picture of a meaningful life in a real society, not a utopia for whose sake a bloodbath was justified as a means to an end.

In *The Human Condition*, Arendt offers a somewhat idealized model of Athenian democracy because it offers democracy as an active work-in-process. She suggests that life consists of Labor (not just physical, but anything that is for the mere purpose of existence; making money, no matter how much), Work (the life of the craft person who seeks to make enduring things, whether it be carpentry or art or word-craft) and Action (of the participant in the life of politics in a democracy). Her interest is in what makes a meaningful life, and to her, participatory politics is the highest human activity. To make that accessible to people, we must practice politics on a scale where people can make a difference. That has been the magic of grassroots movements, but also the bitter disappointment when "dark money" corrupts government.

But on what basis do we make wise choices? On this central subject of philosophy, philosophers since Aristotle have had surprisingly little to say. With Christianity, purity displaced prudence. Then narrow science, runaway technology, and voracious capitalism brought us to the brink of disaster, if not already past the threshold of no return.

What is wisdom?

Let it begin, as it truly does, in uncertainty. But let us remember that uncertainty is not merely a check on our arrogant pretense to knowing. Rather it is the fundamental openness of being, where stone cracks and water flows, where stone cracks and a tender plant springs up in the crevice.

Uncertainty is the condition of all life. It is the matrix for life's growing complexity.

Reinventing Philosophy
Part Four

The most difficult and important problem in the history of human thought is to understand change. How can something change? If it does, is it even the same thing? The problem has been with us since Heraclitus said you can never step in the same river twice; or, perhaps more accurately, that in the same river, ever different waters flow. Unfortunately, though, Parmenides won the debate about time, insisting that change was an intolerable contradiction. Underlying every apparent change was a deeper constancy: an intellectual game that, by definition, subordinates change to constancy rather than seeing them as interdependent.

The great paradox of Western civilization – when it has not simply been Western barbarism – is that its doctrinal denial of time has gone along with – has aided and abetted – its destruction of the environment, threatening the whole web of life that supports us. The great Faustian bargain of Western industrialism – our all-consuming restlessness, the slash-and-burn of an endless yet actually finite frontier – has been built on an intellectual foundation that posits matter as passive. Apparent change is really inertia, force applied to a mere object. When we want to explain change, be it a rocket or a revolution, we look for a force which made whatever happened happen. This view, rooted in simple mechanics, is of course blind to the side effects. Its day of great success depended on limits of which we were unaware. The larger network of benign relationships in the biosphere continued to support us until we broke it and became its fateful custodians.

Western philosophy, in other words, has never been what it pretended to be: an exercise in pure logical inquiry of the "big questions" of human existence: time, free will, the meaning of life, the foundation of ethics, and the basis for a just society, even the existence or not of God. The inquiry, from the days of Plato to Wittgenstein, placed inordinate faith in language, without accounting for the inherent biases of language itself. A shell-shocked young Wittgenstein exploded all philosophic inquiry of two millennia as mere artefacts of language, and inherently meaningless. As Wittgenstein grew older, he became intrigued by the creativity of what he called "language games." But he never opened the windows to the world beyond. We have just discussed three alternative philosophers of the early Twentieth Century: Henri Bergson, Alfred North Whitehead, and Martin Heidegger. Yet mainstream philosophy, especially in British and American universities, contrived to dismiss them as romantics, throwbacks rather than innovators.

Step back, and we realize that the great debates of philosophy were never matters of language alone. Deeper than language and logic was physical intuition: a model upon which philosophic (and much other) thought was based. Greek thought was essentially architectural: it was based on imposing a design, whose justice and beauty consisted in static relationships. Greek architecture timelessly expresses the Golden Ratio: the short side is to the long side as the long side is to the two combined. This may be a static relationship that we apprehend in a moment's glance at a Greek temple, but it also encapsulates a potentially unending process recursively applying the magic ratio, like nested Russian dolls, embodying Goethe's observation that architecture is frozen music.

As long as architecture remained the unexpressed framework for philosophy, philosophy could not grasp change, which depends upon, or requires, a model of self-organization. With the 17th Century, an alternative model became available: the machine. The word "machine" itself is related to "magic" and carries an element of wonder. Hamlet, speaking in exaggeratedly poetic style to Ophelia, says "Whilst this machine is thine" referring to himself and his devotion to her; there is no sense here of himself as a mechanical Frankenstein monster. La Métrie, a philosopher of the age of Descartes, triumphantly calls "Man a Machine." To put this outrageous proposition in its most positive light, it means that the human body works by definite, potentially comprehensible and specific, physical processes. Today, in the age of cyborgs, we are again unsure of the boundary, if any, between the mechanical and the organic. But, shorn of the hyperbole of commerce, the stubborn distinction between machines and organisms remains, and it is the differences that are the key to our growing understanding of life. Machines are designed and assembled out of finished, potentially replaceable, parts. Organisms grow, not out of parts but from whole embryos that begin as undifferentiated totipotent cells into creatures with distinguishable limbs and nervous systems. Machines improve when engineers change the blueprint. Organisms evolve. Despite the facile comparison of the genetic code to a blueprint or computer program, organic evolution is radically different. The differences are of great importance in their own right, but they interest me chiefly as clues to an intellectual model of much wider application.

The most important difference between life and machines is the dialectal (that is, contrastive yet interdependent) relationship between development (that is, the growth of an individual from a single cell to a differentiated adult) and evolution (the historical relatedness of species and their transformation one into another). The genetic code is not a blueprint of an organism, because the DNA is not a picture of a finished machine, and segments of DNA do not, in any simple, separable way, refer to the parts of an organism as parts of a blueprint refer to parts of the machine. Even the most reductionist geneticist would protest, "But no one said they were," but reductionist genetics has created the myths of popular genetics that, as philosopher Mary Midgley among others warned, have immense power as cultural myths. There is no gene just for your toe, much less for your kindness. There is no à la carte map of the organism.

The evolutionary significance of this developmental difference is huge. Even if you can change an organism one gene at a time, that doesn't mean you can change it once characteristic at a time – or even that evolution (natural selection of random change) can do so.

The paradox of evo-devo (the intersection of evolutionary and developmental biology) is that its limitations turn out to be hidden advantages. When, as with God, "all things are possible," many things are actually impossible. By contrast, in the messy, awkward world of life, many things are impossible, but some things – the creative ones – turn out to be possible when they would not otherwise have been.

Seemingly, the great problem of human thought is to understand design without a Designer. And seemingly, Darwin solved it with the combination of random variation (later understood to come from random genetic variation_ combined with natural selection. Darwin got the idea of natural selection from the deliberate breeding of domesticated animals and plants. What if the natural environment did the same thing, selecting what was most advantageous? Darwin's friend Thomas Henry Huxley called it "the survival of the fittest," and it became the basis for Social Darwinism.

But here is the problem. The survival of the fittest depends on what contemporary biologist Andreas Wagner calls the "arrival of the fittest." That is, evolutionary selection can work only on variation that it gets offered. And change is not always incrementally advantageous. It is obviously advantageous to fly, but what use is half a wing? If characteristics must develop by gradual selection of incremental change, how could you ever get a wing big enough actually to life a bird airborne?

Natural selection was arguably the most brilliant idea in the history of human thought, because for the first time it allowed people at least to glimpse the interplay of order and chance. But like most liminal ideas, it was Janus-faced, and the notion of nature *selecting* was far from a harmless transposed metaphor. It still carried far too much of the notion of purpose and obscured how creative change really works without it. This is why the problem of half-a-wing is grist to the mill of religious fundamentalists hunting for Intelligent Design with God as the Designer.

But the real solution is to stop imagining that half a wing got selected for being a proto-wing. What if the poor animal was hot and had a pretty good fan, and as the fan got bigger and better, it gradually became a functional wing?

Wouldn't it be nice to fly like angels? Yes, but the body parts to make wings are employed as arms. Would we really prefer wings to arms? Hands, with opposable thumbs, have been intimately involved in all that is human, in the world we build around us and in the reciprocal development of human intelligence. In the flesh-and-blood world of real creatures, angels would not only be too heavy to fly, even if they had wings; they would also be massively stupid.

Darwin, as we have noted, observed that blue-eyed cats are invariably deaf. What has deafness got to do with being blue-eyed? Nothing, but clearly they are somehow connected in their developmental pathways. We may call this connection a constraint – in this case, it keeps cats from being blue-eyed without paying the price of deafness, and so blue-eyed cats are rare.

We thus easily understand constraint as negative. What is much less apparent to us is constraint as integral to the creativity of life.

Once you dispose of the notion of life as the work of a divine Designer (a notion undermined by life's many quirks, from back pain to appendicitis), you have somehow to explain the world in all its astonishing diversity and complexity. As Harvard biologist and historian of science Stephen Jay Gould notes in *The Structure of Evolutionary Theory,* evolutionary theories divide into externalist and internalist. Darwin's is heavily externalist. He posits a completely plastic (malleable) substance poured into the mold supplied by Natural Selection.

Gould calls the externalist model of Natural Selection "the Panglossian Paradigm." Voltaire's Dr. Pangloss (a caricature of the philosopher Leibnitz in his satire *Candide)* proclaimed that we lived in the best of all possible worlds – a doctrine that was music to the ears of Leibnitz's reactionary patrons.

Applied to Darwinian evolution, the Panglossian paradigm (which is sometimes called Ultra Darwinism, i.e., more Darwinian than Darwin himself) sees creatures as solutions to environmental problems. This is true inasmuch as we all have to live: if we do not solve the problem of getting food, defending ourselves, and finding a mate well enough to leave progeny, then we and our genes disappear. But as biologist Daniel Milo writes in his book *Good Enough,* "Natural Selection has fashioned beautiful works, but it also tolerates a great deal of mediocrity." We should be thankful for it, because otherwise we might not even be here to appreciate its wonders – nor might the wonders.

To think of life as merely struggle in which lucky genes win the lottery and come up with solutions to a fixed set of environmental problems ignores the fact that almost every environmental problem we have is set, not by rocks and stars, but by other living creatures. Who says our solutions are the only ones possible, given astronomy and geology, or even given our particular genes? Karl Marx, in a letter to his friend Friedrich Engels, remarked with amusement that Darwin had applied 19th Century capitalism to the physical and biological world. But Marx himself clothed his communist utopia in a spurious determinism and in the process handed the likes of Josef Stalin with a pretext for murder, both in the Moscow Trials and in the forced collectivization of farms, with brought starvation to millions.

Praise be to imperfection; praise be to contingency – and acknowledgement of it.

It is the incompleteness of nature at one level that leads to its achievements on the next. Atoms with a complete set of electrons in their outer ring are known as "noble"; but it is atoms with incomplete rings of electrons that bond as molecules. Open systems that we are, we are bound, as Lear puts it, on a wheel of fire, obliged to seek beyond ourselves just to stay alive, like Alice's Red Queen, who must run merely to stay in place. It is a paradox, but no mystery, that you don't need *the universe* to have purpose; on the contrary, systems with purpose arise spontaneously in a universe of process.

The interdependence of ontogeny (development from a single fertilized cell to an adult) and phylogeny (the historical evolution and transformation of creatures) is as creative as it is often mediocre. It gives biology a holiday from the tyranny of having to be advantageous in each increment of change. If every creature with half a wing had gone extinct, evolution would never have given us birds.

In the case of birds, wings owe their existence to dual function (as fans, useful before the wing is functional for flight). But other cases show the reorganization of development as the decisive change. Take the evolution of human beings.

At some point in the dim past, apes (or some of them, our ancestors) came down from the trees. In pursuit of game, some learned to knuckle walk on all fours. But the revolutionary change came when someone stood upright. After millions of years, we are still not very good at that, making us the animal who walks on four legs in the morning, two at noon, and three in the evening. One change – our posture – rewarded another – growing intelligence. That brought bigger brains and bigger heads, beyond the capacity of the mother's birth canal.

"Oh Gertrude," exclaims Claudius, Hamlet's usurping uncle, "when sorrows come, they come not as single spies, but in battalions." And so it is with evolutionary change. A la carte menus are rare and expensive. Evolution rarely conjures up merely what it "wants" (what is the evolutionary characteristic that would be advantageous and is therefore selective). The economical tourist takes the *prix fixe,* and evolution most economically adjusts relative rates of development. The most powerful evolutionary-developmental change is to adjust the rate at which we mature – notably, by slowing it down.

Paedomorphosis (meaning "child-formed"), sometimes known as neotony, is the slowing down of one rate of growth, sexual maturity, relative to other growth, notably of our brains. By staying immature longer, we have more time to grow bigger brains. The biologist Aldous Huxley wrote a playful novel about an American millionaire who hired a mad scientist to make him live forever. That was easy. The potion turned him into an adult ape. We are baby chimps grown large.

But what makes us human is not the growth of intelligence alone, or even that primarily. Are other infants born crying? Our paedomorphosis means that human infants come into the world in a singular state of helplessness. That requires intense parental care, prolonged learning (potentially of socially learned knowledge, not merely biologically innate skills), and societies that can foster nurture. Nurture *is* our nature, and with it, a great range of potential societies and ways of being human. The notion of evolution red in tooth and claw, the result of sheer ruthless competition, could never have led to human society, or even to so called rugged individualist "self-made" capitalists.

As E.O. Wilson, the doyen of social insects, notes, humans are a social species. But in recent years, Wilson, father of sociobiology, has had the humility and wisdom to say that human sociality is radically different from the beehives and ant hills on which he cut his teeth.

Sacrifice for the common good can be explained in exact genetic terms in the social insects. Their sacrifice is not in any real sense generous; it is robotic. But although it is true that humans prefer kin to outsiders, the preference is not on the basis of genes, but of close bonding association.

The conventional thinker says, "First learn the basics," and you spend most of a career studying the reductionist building blocks. More intangible considerations are luxuries for the memoirs of Nobel laureates, read with a by younger, hard-driving colleagues.

Human compassion is not a luxury add-on to the atomically complete, closed selfish individual. Rather, our social bonding is a result of our incompleteness, our vulnerability, our spontaneous identification with the plight and suffering of others.

The paradigm of evolution casts light on human creativity, and human creativity casts light on evolution. A couple of creativity researchers, Drew Boyd and Jacob Goldenberg, waggishly call their book *Inside the Box*. "We believe that you'll be most creative," they write, "when you focus on the internal aspects of a situation or problem – and when you constrain your options rather than broaden them. By defining and then closing the boundaries of a particular creative challenge and then looking only inside these boundaries, you can be more creative more consistently than by musing about the stratosphere or, worse, waiting for the muse to descend." How ironic that by thinking "Inside the Box," Boyd and Goldenberg did just what they warned against: they thought outside the box.

Whichever side of the fence (or box) they are really on, Boyd and Goldenberg remind us of a truth we just encountered in human evolution: radical change comes not from importing a shiny new element but from a seemingly slight reorganization of existing elements or processes – in that case, paedomorphosis, the prolongation of childhood, permitting the brain and mind to continue developing longer. (Notably, even human pets – such as dogs – tend to be paedomorphic, making them more playful and attaching their childlike dependency to us.) Our childish, or child-like, nature leaves us willing to follow authorities of our own creation, for good and for bad.

What makes Shakespeare the most original of Elizabethan dramatists if not of all verbal artists? Oxford Shakespeare scholar Jonathan Bate points to two differences between Shakespeare and his university-educated contemporaries such as Ben Jonson and Christopher Marlowe. Shakespeare was in the first instance a rewrite guy. Almost every play is a rewrite. Secondly, unlike his more scholarly rivals, Shakespeare was first and foremost a theater professional, and the reality of the theater is dominant in all of his plays. It becomes his objective correlative for the human condition. "All the world's a stage" is a conceit of course, but it also captures the paradox that unlike most creatures, which have fixed behaviors, humans are actors who must take a role to enter the great play of human society. At the same time, the audience is sitting in a theater watching a real actor playing an imaginary character proclaim he is just an actor. Which is appearance and which is reality? It is impossible to say. We are caught in the creative ambiguity of the human condition.

Technology depends on exactitude for its illusion of realism: sharper and sharper images and more and more dimensions. But that is almost the opposite of what artists often do. A few brushstrokes or lines are enough. They captivate us because – as the great art critic E. H. Gombrich points out in his famous book *Art and Illusion* – the image is almost always ambiguous. We must be participants in creating the image. Not technological completeness, but artistic incompleteness, brings us into the web of creative uncertainty. Walter Isaacson, discussing Leonardo's Mona Lisa, notes that her smile is inconsistent with the rest of her expression, and that is what makes her so fascinating.

Perhaps the fundamental problem of creativity – be it evolutionary, artistic, social, or political, is to create the environment that fosters creativity. It is a recursive process: we have to be creative to make the world that makes us creative. Yet it is not an impossible task, because the spark lives with all of us, the spark of chaos-making, disorganization followed by reorganization, what Whitehead called order entering upon novelty.

Those who have genius are those willing to risk everything, willing to let genius (or spirit) *have* them. With what courage Beethoven let heartbreak and chaos seize him in the late quartets and sonatas, to weave them into savage fugues that are not, like Bach's, preexisting solutions to tidy if difficult problems, but are truly unforeseeable creations.

Change takes courage because to be true, change must almost always be deleterious. The way to new adaptation lies through ill adaptation. In a world of universal competition and natural selection, how is this ever possible? Here lies the principle of island biogeography. When through climate change, for example, a population becomes somewhat separated from the larger gene pool, inefficient variants or experiments have a better chance to become established. They may then rejoin the larger population as new species. To be a big fish in a big pond, you probably need first to be a relatively big fish in a small pond.

We quoted earlier the withering reductionist Jacques Monod, who sees humans as very small fish in an infinite ocean, "wandering on the edge of an alien world, a world that is deaf to our music, just as indifferent to our hopes as it is to our suffering or our crimes." But in order to diminish us, Monod had himself to take a God's-eye view. He was able to see us as marginal only by assuming that the universe has a center – somewhere else.

Those who, against all evidence, cling to an authoritarian God, and those who are embittered by such a God's non-existence, are caught in a world not worth wanting.

We have a choice. The debate over free will is as old as humanity and as new as the latest brain science, which is startlingly different from the second-latest brain science. The second-latest brain science will tell you that choice is an illusion. Some reflexes, like raising your leg when the doctor taps your knee, actually precede your conscious awareness of them.

But the timing of our awareness of a reflex action (the Benjamin Libet Experiment) is far less significant than deterministic philosophers take it to be. That is not what free will is about anyway. Real freedom is about bigger, vaguer decisions we live with for months or years: whom we will live with, how we will shape our lives. Almost never do we make these choices in one gulp. We live with them. Our freedom may not lie in the instant that we make them (by which time they may not even feel like choices) but in the practices by which we prepare to make them, like a musician preparing for a concert. Brain scientist Peter Ulrich Tse calls this "criterial causation": we set the criteria by which we choose in the moment. This model is strikingly like Aristotle's, two thousand years ago, of cultivating virtues.

Today the choice facing us at every moment and on every scale is between the nurture of life and the heedless plunge to extinction. We do not know whether we are alone in the universe or even whether our universe is alone in the cosmos or is one amid a multiverse. What we do know is that whether or not we are alone, we are unique, and the choice between destruction and creativity is ours to make.

8 Beyond Resilience

Toward his death, my father often said that his generation had been the most abject failure of any generation in human history. That was a bleak assessment of the "Greatest Generation" of Americans, who had fought in World War II and devoted their lives to public service. But John felt their public service had been fatally compromised by the self-interest and self-righteousness that he experienced in sickening fashion in his own role in the coup in Brazil, in his colleagues' involvement in Vietnam, and most of all in his contemporaries' smug self-enrichment in the years following. Now, it is hard to disagree that the last forty years of militarism, hyper capitalism, and environmental recklessness have taken the world past the point of no return, most of all on climate change.

We can thus no longer offer a simple Either/Or: "Either you must do this, or there will be a catastrophe." On the other hand, fatalism -- "We are over the falls; it is too late to do anything," -- simply replaces one excuse with another. On climate change, in particular, disastrous changes are already underway – heat, drought, fire, rising sea levels, extinctions, pandemics, mass migration, and wars – all sure to get worse over the century. Nevertheless, it matters enormously what we do: the range of outcomes stretches from the very challenging, to the virtually complete loss of life on Earth.

We must thus combine prevention (or mitigation, as it is sometimes called) with resilience. Resilience is defined as a system's ability to bounce back after a setback. It is most common in the vocabulary, or jargon, of popular psychology, and is a feature of the "be more" school that goes with worthy programs of physical and mental fitness, as if resilience were a superior form of strength. As such, the pop psychology version easily gives rise to a complete misunderstanding, because resilience is all about weakness – and an acknowledgment of it. Resilience begins in the recognition of failure.

Resilience inevitably involves a sacrifice of adaptation on behalf of adaptability. The economist Herbert Simon tells the fable of two watchmakers, Bios and Mekhos. Mekhos builds his watches (with hundreds of parts) part by part, adding each to his blueprint of the whole. Bios builds her watch in units (sub-assemblies) ten parts at a time. When Mekhos is interrupted, the whole structure collapses and he must start again. When Bios is interrupted, she has merely lost a small subassembly. In a world of distractions – ringing telephones, customers entering the shop, or worse (but after Simon's day) Internet browsing --, Mekhos never manages to finish a watch. Bios, whose method is predicated on interruption, is the superior watchmaker.

But something is wrong with this allegory, as it is with the title and concept of Richard Dawkins's sophisticated but reductionist book on evolution, "The Blind Watchmaker." Life, aka Bios, does not make watches. Perhaps Herbert Simon is proposing an elementary form of biomimicry: human invention modeled on nature. And that is what this book is proposing: that unlike machines (or the mechanist paradigm) the pattern of living things is naturally intertwined with uncertainty, error, mishap, and sometimes with catastrophe. Yet we must push this thesis past the resting point of smugness.

Organisms are not, in fact, "built" out of completed sub-assemblies of ten parts each. In the case of animals, which are unlike plants in this respect, they begin with a whole and over time differentiate into a multicellular, more complex whole. Divide a sea urchin, and it regenerates as two sea urchins. A human embryo that divides before fertilization by a sperm makes twins; right after fertilization, it makes identical twins. But Solomon's famous command to cut the infant in half was a test to identify the real mother, not a way to satisfy each claimant. A frog can regenerate a lost limb. A horse cannot, and in *Anna Karenina*, the heartbreaking scene of Vronsky's racehorse Frou Frou breaking her leg ends with Frou Frou being shot. Fortunately, we do not shoot people who lose limbs in landmines; we offer them prosthetics. Thus the real story of organic resilience is a lot more complicated than Herbert Simon's neat fable of Bios and Mekhos.

Indeed, it is vital to recognize that organic systems can be shockingly lacking in resilience. The Amazon rainforest is the planet's greatest treasure of bio-diversity, and its lush vegetation has been called Earth's lung. You would think, then, that the forest was a paragon of resilience. But though it contributes invaluably to the planet's resilience, the rainforest itself is heartbreakingly vulnerable. Like an individual organism, when attacked, it dies. It is self-maintaining because its nutrients are held in its roots and its moisture is preserved by its trees. Cut it down for plantation soybeans and cattle ranching, as corporate landowners do: it dies, and what remains is soon barren cement. Even more surprisingly, its fantastic diversity is itself fragile. When a particular fig tree is cross pollinated by a particular kind of wasp, you have a lock-and-key system of mutual vulnerability. Its stunning diversity emerged from fecundity, competition, and specialization. It shatters when seriously disrupted.

The metaphor of Gaia – the entire global ecosystem as a living system, indeed an organism – is both illuminating and dangerously misleading. It is true that during the recent geological period of the Holocene – the period that human interference has now destroyed – Earth's coupled living systems formed a self-regulatory system that maintained a stable climate despite changing incoming solar energy. But while a feedback loop of organisms may in some ways resemble an organism, it is not one, and it has no intentions or purposes. What it does have is various zones of stability – the equivalent of separated valleys between mountain peaks. When disturbance pushes it out of one valley, there is no assurance it will return. In short, even if Gaia lives, there is no assurance that Earth will remain habitable for humans or complex animals. Paradoxically, the advent of the Anthropocene may well be the end for humans, which, in any natural sense, are a very young species that should be just in the beginning of their natural history, a period in which our recorded history is merely a few minutes in a long day.

To survive the coming shocks, we must build our resilience. But what, again, is resilience? We said resilience is a sacrifice of perfect adaptation for the sake of adaptability. The fragility of the Amazon or of the depth of the ocean is stability, which has permitted complex, perfect adaptation – but a lot of broken china in an earthquake.

The watchword of resilience, as in Bios's way of building watches in small subassemblies, is decoupling: the failure of one subassembly does not destroy the others or bring down the whole network. Consider the classic case of the outage of an electric grid. In a system that is too tightly coupled, a local outage can cause a blackout of the Eastern United States, as happened in the famous Northeast blackout of 1967. In the terms of Yale sociologist Charles Perrow in his book *Normal Accidents,* complex, tightly coupled systems – be it the Chernobyl nuclear reactor or the Apollo 13 spacecraft – are error-intolerant: errors cascade unforeseeably. A wrench dropped in the tube of a Titan nuclear missile in Damascus, Arkansas silo caused the missile, loaded with a nuclear warhead, to launch, though fortunately the warhead did not detonate.

"Only connect the prose and the passion," pleads Margaret Schlegel in E. M. Forster's *Howard's End,* "and both will be exalted, and human love will be seen at its highest. Live in fragments no longer." That may also sound like an ecologist's mantra for an interdependent Earth.

But a wag, thinking of resilient, adaptable ecosystems, inverted the advice: "Only disconnect." If you are not all dependent on one massive nuclear power plant, but there are many sources of renewable energy, the network is safer – provided that there isn't an uncanny rhythmic coupling that itself brings down the grid. A row of poplars in cross sunlight can cause a strobe effect and epileptic seizure. Tightly spaced trees are prone to fire and pests. Crowded, filthy livestock fed antibiotics in CAFOs (confined animal feeding operations, which are animal concentration camps) only breed anti-biotic resistant germs, which then jump to human hospitals.

Yet as the Covid 19 pandemic illustrates, the relationship between human density and ultimate diversity is not simple. In the first instance, it was dense settlements, such as New York City, that were vulnerable, while rural America watched with detachment. But then secular urbanites started wearing masks, which anti-science Trump supporters in the Heartland refused to do, and the relationship reversed. The moral is that in complex systems in which humans are involved, you can no longer just look at a physical disposition: we ourselves are a vital part of the resilience, or of its lack. A divided nation where uneducated whites are failing to meet expectations and dying "deaths of despair" is a threat to its own physical and political health. It is struggling to meet an overdue reckoning on America's founding sin of racial injustice.

Indeed, a simplistic environmentalist ideology has a way, instead, of being capitalist ideology. Consider the famous "Malthusian trap" of rising population and scarce resources. In it, food can at best increase arithmetically, while population increases exponentially, till an original Adam and Eve outbreed the Earth. It may be well to remember that Thomas Malthus was a reactionary who thought it inevitable that the poor would starve and advisable that the propertied classes let them do so sooner rather than later. It was Malthus, combined with the example of domesticated animal breeding, whose ideas Darwin brilliantly fused into Natural Selection: competition (like the Malthusian squeeze) "chose" the fittest, as the domestic dog or horse breeder selects for desired characteristics. Darwin, unlike the Social Darwinists, was a kind man, but already the implication was not lost on Karl Marx, who saw a mirror for 19th Century capitalist ideology.

Likewise, the grim ecologist Garrett Hardin proposed "lifeboat ethics" for an overpopulated planet. In this fable, it is one added African or Indian who sinks the lifeboat, not the American who consumes a hundred times more.

To illustrate tragic inevitability, Garrett Hardin proposed a fable of "The Tragedy of the Commons." Each sheep farmer stands to gain, by putting more than their share of sheep on the commons, until the commons are depleted and everyone starves. Yet historically, people starved when the commons were enclosed for the benefit of large property holders. As scholar-activist David Bollier says in his book, *Think Like a Commoner,* the real commons was not unregulated; it did have rules and did not allow the greedy to take advantage of it. Hardin, says Bollier, is providing a paradigm not of a true commons but of an unregulated capitalist market.

The scholar who did the most to convey an understanding of a true commons was Indiana University's Elinor Ostrom, who studied real commons in non-industrialized societies. She and her husband, Vince Ostrom, found that the success of the commons was interdependent with the social strength of the group, permitting real but not formally codified communal regulation. (Such regulation has no loopholes.)

But what happens when not only commoners are on the commons? Can you expect the sheep to nibble grass when a wolf is on the prowl? David Bollier notes that Elinor Ostrom mostly studied small scale natural commons such as forests. As the scale increases, so does the attraction to a wolf. At that point, the informal regulation by cooperative smallholders is no match for a giant multinational corporation with its ability to buy out a few, coerce others to sell "in time," and to bribe regulators. In today's world, any paradigm predicated on a healthy commons is a dream until the reality of predatory capitalism is powerfully addressed.

Yet that by no means assures us that capitalist ideology is somehow realistic. For one thing, classical economics is all about "value added" in production. It treats non-renewable resources such as fossil fuels and irreplaceable assets – clean water, clean air, and a stable climate – as mere incidentals. Governmental regulation, in this view, threatens to kill the goose that lays the golden eggs – as if the reality were not the other way round: the entire framework of a benign nature is approaching the threshold of collapse, and though a more chaotic nature continues to interact as a dynamic system, it is no longer benign: thus the rising sea level, hurricanes, droughts, fires, famines, and wars that mark the period we are entering and whose force, even in the best of circumstances, can only increase in the coming century or centuries.

Nuclear weapons, along with climate change, are one of the twin existential threats that could end life on Earth. Today, the world has nine nuclear nations: the United States, Russia, the United Kingdom, France, China, India, Pakistan, Israel, and North Korea. A war between India and Pakistan alone would kill billions of people globally, not only those who died of blast, firestorms, and radiation, but many more months later as lofted dust darkened the skies and a nuclear winter killed crops and brought global famine.

The United States and Russia together control 91% of the world's nuclear arsenals, so our call to keep nuclear weapons out of the hands of so-called "rogue states" meets with cries of hypocrisy. Nor did the danger of nuclear war with Russia die with the Cold War and the demise of the Soviet Union in 1991. Indeed, many experts think the danger is as great today as it was in the two worst moments of the Cold War: the Cuban Missile Crisis of 1962 and Operation Able Archer of 1983.

"Nuclear weapons," said Einstein, "have changed everything save our ways of thinking, and thus we drift toward unparalleled catastrophe." Nuclear weapons not only threaten humanity; they also spoil war. The 18th Century theorist of war Carl Friedrich von Clausewitz famously said that war is the continuation of politics by other means. But it is less well known that he added that when war ceases to serve political ends, it becomes senseless. A weapon that is omnicidal is, by definition, also suicidal.

And yet the whole enormously lucrative business of nuclear designers and manufacturers since 1945 has been in denial of the brutal truth of the atomic age. How barbaric to aim huge thermonuclear warheads at population centers, a crime thousands of times worse than the Nazi Blitz on London, the Allied bombing of Dresden, or the American fire-bombing of Tokyo! What if we could make much more accurate missiles and smaller, more precise nuclear warheads? What if we replaced blunt "counter-value" targeting, which is nuclear revenge, a promise to commit an act of violence that would be senseless when you actually did it, with "counter-force" targeting, attacking the other country's missiles, not people, and, best of all, attacking them before they were fired, sparing your own country? It sounds eminently humane, and, best of all, if you really had such a capability, it would make nuclear weapons "usable" again, something we could use not just to deter Moscow from a full scale nuclear attack on New York, Chicago, and Los Angeles, but, say, a Putin power grab invading Ukraine, Lithuania, or Poland? It's a sign of just how seductive this logic is that it is associated with one of the best and most compassionate human beings ever to be President of the United States: Jimmy Carter. Presidential Directive 59, otherwise known as the Carter Doctrine, says the United States will use "any means necessary" to "protect" the Persian Gulf and the "free" flow of oil, which it is the mission of the leading imperialist power to secure on behalf of the world's democracies (that is, subordinate capitalist nations).

Ronald Reagan, who had defeated Carter with the avuncular "There you go again" when Carter warned of the danger of an all-out U.S.-U.S.S.R. nuclear arms race, embarked on an enormous nuclear buildup that brought the world at least as close to the brink of nuclear war as we had been during the Cuban Missile crisis of 1962. Three times during 1983, errors, by accident or on purpose or some mix, brought us to the edge, in the context of an ailing Soviet leadership and one alarmed by the U.S. nuclear buildup. On September 1st, a Korean Airliner, coincidentally named Flight 007, flew hundreds of miles off course from its normal New York – Anchorage – Tokyo –Seoul route and directly over sensitive Soviet military sites on Kamchatka and the main Soviet nuclear submarine port of Sakhalin. The Soviets claimed it was accompanied by U.S. military spy planes and was designed to give the U.S. the technical intelligence it would need to penetrate Soviet air defenses in a nuclear first strike. At any rate, Soviet forces were in a state of panic that night and apparently shot down the airliner, killing all 262 passengers and 7 crew.

Three weeks later, Soviet nuclear launch officers received word that U.S. missiles were on the way and they had only minutes to fire back before their forces would be destroyed. The Soviet launch commander, Stanislav Petrov, unable to get denial or confirmation, made the personal decision not to fire, earning U.N. Secretary General Kofi Annan's later praise as "the man who saved the world." It turned out that the glint of the setting sun on some mirrors had activated Soviet satellites, which mistook the flash for a U.S. nuclear missile launch.

Later that autumn, a NATO military exercise, Operation Able Archer, simulated a Western nuclear attack on the Soviet Union. The Soviets, meanwhile, had a plan for a real nuclear attack on the West disguised at first as just a military exercise. They came very close to firing their nuclear weapons on the principle of "use them or lose them." The experience apparently chastened Reagan and left him prepared to agree with Gorbachev that "nuclear war cannot be won and must not be fought."

But when the Soviet Union collapsed, some Western analysts proclaimed "Victory," not for democracy, but for the American nuclear buildup. The nuclear arms race had forced the infirm Soviet economy into a spending race it could not afford, so it was American hawkishness that supposedly won the Cold War. Never mind that it corrupted American democracy, weakened our economy, and helped distract us for a crucial generation from the other existential crisis, climate change, that it is now too late to avoid.

I have discussed the nuclear arms race not just because it is a vastly underestimated existential threat but also because it illustrates the limits of any facile doctrine of resilience. Resilience, as an ethos of "Gumptionade," in the title of an Amazon.com book listed in its "resilience" collection, is not much use with nuclear war, where we would at best be left, in Jonathan Schell's phrase, with "a republic of insects and grass," though in Schell's day the impact on climate was not understood. We might not have even insects and grass.

But we are too addicted to stop. As Daniel Ellsberg notes, every President since the Second World War has used U.S. nuclear weapons in the sense that pointing a loaded revolver is to use it, even if you do not pull the trigger. My father used to warn me against bluffing. Don't make a threat you are not prepared to carry out, he used to say. If someone calls your bluff, you will be in the worst of dilemmas: either you look weak, or you have to carry out a threat that is against your own interest. Yet for years the West's defense of Western Europe rested on a nuclear threat. Worse, after the breakup of the Warsaw Pack, the U.S. broke its pledge and extended NATO to the East. Would we launch a nuclear attack on Russia over Lithuania, thereby unleashing a nuclear war and total destruction of life on Earth?

Nuclear weapons manufacturers have the answer: that is why we need "low yield" nuclear warheads, so that we can make the "calibrated" and "credible" threat of a "limited" nuclear strike. In the words of the late Senator Richard Lugar, former Defense Secretary William Perry, and others: "It is doubtful there is such a thing as limited nuclear war, and preparing for one is folly." Or as Daniel Ellsberg says in his powerful book *The Doomsday Machine*, "It is virtually certain that a single U.S. nuclear weapon landing on Russia or single Russian nuclear weapon landing on the United States would unleash a full scale nuclear war, ending all life on Earth."

But what would you do if you knew that limited nuclear war is a fantasy but you thought the Russians believed in it? Or if you were a Russian and you thought the Americans did? Wouldn't you then yourself have to take such threats seriously, lest you call their bluff but they went through with it anyway? And if that is so, then what about the converse: isn't there an important strategic advantage to be gained by pretending to believe in limited nuclear war and even actually building the weapons to make the threat "credible"? Shouldn't the other side have to bear the burden of strategic uncertainty? As a boy, I used to break chicken wish bones with a stern banker uncle. I learned not to pull the bone my way but to push it up his way, and his side of the bone would reliably break. For all the stakes – which are literally the fate of the Earth – nuclear strategy is remarkably subjective, not to mention childish.

Barack Obama entered office pledging to work for a world free from nuclear weapons, a pledge which helped him win the Nobel Prize at the beginning of his Presidency. Eight years later, after many setbacks and capitulations, he wanted to leave office with at least one accomplishment in that direction. He had achieved the nuclear deal with Iran but wanted to declare that the United States would never be the first to use nuclear weapons in a conflict. His cabinet and the military talked him out of it.

And so the United States remains committed to initiate nuclear war, not merely in defense of Western Europe, but also to hold our territorial gains after the collapse of communism. What we would actually do in such a situation may be unknown to leaders themselves. Thus the logic of "The Doomsday Machine": to reap the benefit of making incredible threats, good acting is not enough: you must set the tripwire automatically. In Stanley Kubrick's devastating satire, the Russians cannot stop launching a world-ending nuclear attack even when the President tells them the American bomber headed their way is unauthorized. In fact, this absurdist twist was entirely true – and remains so. The problem with a security system based on layers of insanity is, of course, the risk of miscalculation – think of 1914.

When the United States had a monopoly on nuclear weapons, they seemed to compensate for our unwillingness or inability to fight bloody conventional wars. We used atomic weapons on Hiroshima and Nagasaki at least in part not to have to invade Japan – though critical historians such as Gar Alperowitz argue that the Japanese were prepared to surrender and the real purpose of the atomic bombing was to intimidate the Soviets. (It actually spurred Stalin to get the bomb himself.) Likewise, we maintained that NATO nuclear weapons were needed to keep Stalin from rolling his tanks to Paris as Hitler had done – though diplomats tried to tell Washington that a wounded Soviet Union was more concerned with brutal domination of its near abroad as a buffer than with distant conquest and settlement on the Hitler model.

The idea of nuclear weapons as a substitute for conventional forces invites a question: "If you are so worried about nuclear weapons, why not build up conventional forces instead?" But the world of 1947 is long gone, and "conventional" forces are no longer conventional. The United States now has overwhelming technological dominance in high tech non-nuclear forces. With a capability called Prompt Global Strike, Washington can hit any location anywhere in the world within minutes, and we are especially good at "taking out," that is, decapitating, a nation's leadership. Nations such as North Korea and Iran have this incentive to go nuclear: it is the only reliable way to deter an American war of regime change.

After completing his powerful anti-nuclear book *The Fate of the Earth* in the 1980s, Jonathan Schell came to realize that you can no longer solve the problem of nuclear weapons without addressing the larger problem of war itself. In a world where nuclear weapons offer a so called rogue state relatively cheap security, you cannot end the global nuclear threat without offering some form of security other than imperialism. The notion of America as the "indispensable nation" leading a global order of McDonald's outlets fails because of various forms of asymmetric warfare, to which our only answer is a global sky looming with American drones ready to annihilate a wedding party anywhere on Earth if we have "actionable intelligence." It is hard to imagine that such a system will not fail catastrophically in the next generation, on a planet increasingly wracked by inequality, climate change, famine, and mass migration.

It would be foolish, and destructive, to say we cannot change our mortally dangerous nuclear weapons policies unless we first solve all the world's economic and social problems. That is like trying to solve your personal problems by playing Russian roulette. My father had an aide in the U.S. Embassy in Rio who did that one night, drunk, with a Mephistophelean companion. He claimed he thought the chambers were empty before he began the experiment in front of his wife.

There is in fact an eminently sane agenda called Back from the Brink and supported by responsible arms control experts: renounce the first use of nulear weapons; end the President's sole authority to launch a nuclear attack; take nuclear weapons off hair-trigger alert; cancel nuclear weapons "modernization" (enhancement); and enter global negotiations for the verifiable elmination of nuclear weapons.

But what we can say is that stark economic and racial injustice and environmental recklessness, combined with a morbid quest for absolute certainty and security, push leaders and the public to the brink of omnicide.

A few summers ago, I attended a gathering of frequently published *New York Times* letter writers. The next evening, I strolled along East End Avenue across from the United Nations and observed the hierarchy of V.I.P. vehicles: first, the black S.U.V.s with tinted windows; then, one step up, black S.U.V.s preceded by motorcycles; finally, top of the pack, helicopters landing on the roof. How ironic that this institution dedicated to peace and justice is a display of wealth and power. Look across the street and One United Nations Plaza is the ultimate destination residence for the ultra-wealthy, especially since the view of the United Nations and the East River from the lower floors is even more desirable than the sweeping views (of Queens, actually) from top floors. It was dusk, and owners could not be bothered with blinds: the point was to display their trophies. In one living room hung a large brutalist abstract painting of the kind favored by billionaires; on another floor was an enormous gleaming gold Russian icon, perhaps belonging to a gangster oligarch in our out of favor with Vladimir Putin. Extreme wealth in the 21st Century has reached proportions unknown in the 20th but familiar from the days of the Robber Barons or the court of Louis XIV.

There is an old story, probably apocryphal, of Oleg Troyanovsky, a Soviet Ambassador to the United Nations during the Cold War. One day an American right wing demonstrator threw a can of red paint at him, splattering his suit. The unflappable diplomat responded coolly, "Better red than dead."

The story is a reminder that for more than forty years the clash between capitalism and communism was one of the purported reasons for a nuclear confrontation that at any moment could have ended life on Earth. As John F. Kennedy famously said in his Inaugural Address, "We shall pay any price, bear any burden, support any friend, oppose any foe, to ensure the survival and the success of liberty. The cost of freedom is always high, but Americans have always paid it." But by the time of his assassination, after the Cuban Missile Crisis, Kennedy had grown wary of such rhetoric, and in his speech at American University in June 1963, Kennedy called for nuclear disarmament and peace with Russia. One wonders what he would have thought had he known that thirty years after the demise of the Soviet Union, the nuclear standoff would continue. Besides, anyone who can read political rhetoric knows what "freedom" means. Young Americans for Freedom was a Goldwater organization, close to the John Birch Society. Acolytes of right wing Russian émigré Ayn Rand celebrated unbridled capitalism and selfishness. Among them were including her close friend Alan Greenspan, future chief of the Federal Reserve Board.

"Liberty" and "freedom" are mercurial terms, as is "equality." American rhetoric if not American reality has sought to hold them together. In the Gettysburg Address, Abraham Lincoln said the Founding Fathers had conceived this nation in liberty and dedicated it to the proposition that all men are created equal. Yet Lincoln embarked on the Civil War to save the Union, not to end slavery; and the Founders designed the Constitution to thwart the will of the majority, as it continues to do when low population white states in the interior can outweigh much more populous, diverse states on the coasts. A Wyoming voter is 70 times more powerful in choosing a Senator than a voter in California.

There are long periods when societies make do with the contradictions in their founding principles. And there are crisis points when they must revisit and redefine them.

"Freedom is precious," said Lenin – "so precious it must be rationed." The cynicism underlying that statement might have served as a warning about the ultimate fate of the Soviet experiment.

When Lincoln spoke of freedom and equality in the same breath, he could not have known that his Republican Party would not only become the party of the rich but would flip its geographic base to the South and become the party of white supremacy. Meanwhile, the Supreme Court would interpret Constitutional rights to free speech (in the Citizens United case) to mean that corporations could engage in unlimited amounts of campaign spending so that sovereignty lay with dollars not votes. These reversals would have been less surprising to a historian who remembered that slavery was a capitalist institution modeled on British sugar plantations on Barbados, and this practice implicated the mercantile North as well as the pseudo-aristocratic caste system of the South. Racism ensured that poor whites would vent their frustration on even poorer Blacks (and even more, on any Black who dared step out of line) rather than on the leisure class of Sothern white plantation owners.

As Lyndon Johnson once said, "If you can convince the lowest white man he's better than the best colored man, he won't notice you're picking his pocket. Hell, give him somebody to look down on, and he'll empty his pockets for you." This created the brutal politics were working class whites voted for a blatantly corrupt billionaire as their revenge on a more educated and diverse new American meritocracy.

The top 1%'s share of U.S. wealth has risen by half since the late 1970s, while the top 0.1% -- less than 200,000 households with a net worth starting north of $20 million – have doubled their share. During Donald Trump's presidency the collective wealth of American billionaires (166 people) went from $1.8 trillion to $2.8 trillion, and 80% of that increase went to the top fifty.

What do these numbers even mean? Someone with a $238 million New York penthouse is far past the point of diminishing returns, compared with a retired teacher with a small but comfortable apartment, books, and the Internet. Qualitatively, the difference between a middle class person and someone who is homeless and hungry, still less a war refugee in a developing country, is far greater. But the gaps of extreme inequality are still very important as divisions in political power and our ability as a whole society to make decisions about our common future.

To see the deeper significance of inequality, we have to look beyond the surface of news reports at the notion of human morality and society. The anthropologist Michael Tomasello discusses these roots in his book *The Natural History of Human Morality.*

Humans are an intensely social species, but, unlike social insects (ants, bees, termites) our behavior is not hard wired: the complexity of both our brains and of our behavioral choices precludes that. We do, however, have natural moral feelings – feelings that, Tomasello suggests, are ultimately the result of Darwinian selection, because those who behave morally leave more offspring: when everyone is selfish and solitary, the group and therefore its members perish. This does not mean that we *experience* moral feeling in terms of cold evolutionary calculation – any more than we experience sexual desire in terms of the genetic advantage of having children.

As a vegan, I enjoy the irony that so much of human sociality, indeed morality, arises from the hunt. Early humans needed to cooperate to hunt down animals substantially larger than themselves and then to share the prize.

Tomasello suggests that there are several distinct types of moral feeling, which he believes arose from distinct evolutionary situations. One is empathy: we experience another's suffering as our own. Another type he describes as shared intentionality: undertaking a shared project. Finally, he suggests a somewhat more formal feeling, applying to a slightly larger group: fairness. Who deserves a piece of meat? Who is being greedy? Who is lazy, a free-rider who does not deserve a piece at all?

These are never unconflicted feelings. Insofar as they are the implant of evolutionary advantage, they are in obvious tension with sheer self-interests. Those who practice sheer self-abnegation may be good for others, but they leave no heirs. Yet society evolves prosocial norms and honors those who uphold them.

All of this would seem as obvious as common sense; yet common sense itself is by no means obvious, nor is it common sense. In the title by Thomas Paine, "Common Sense" is radical, filled with universal (and egalitarian) human rights. From the lips of Archie Bunker or Donald Trump, however, common sense is cynical self-interest and mockery of anyone pretentious enough to think anyone works on higher principles.

The world has always had its share of cynics, but there was a crucial revolution of values in the early modern period. This was the idea of mechanism. It allowed the individual to be purely selfish. Shakespeare's Iago speaks its creed, addressing the rich young man Roderigo, whom he is fleecing of his money in the vain hope of winning Desdemona: "Oh villainous! I have looked upon the world for four times seven years, and since I could distinguish between a benefit and an injury, I have never found a man that knew how to love himself. If thou wilt needs damn thyself, do it a more delicate way than drowning. Make all the money thou canst."

Roderigo: "I am changed. I'll go sell all my land."

Making this the creed of his most hellish villain, Shakespeare was well aware what a problematic ethic egoism is. But that did not stop early moderns from embracing it.

In the early modern period, economists were professors of Moral Philosophy. Adam Smith's first book is *A Theory of Moral Sentiments,* seeking to strike a balance between self-interest and altruism in each individual human life. His second book, of course, is *The Wealth of Nations,* and it speaks from a different world. "It is not from the benevolence of the butcher, the brewer, or the baker that we expect our dinner, but from their regard to their own interest. We address ourselves, not to their humanity, but to their self-love, and never talk to them of their own necessity, but of their advantages. Nobody but a beggar chooses to depend chooses to depend on the benevolence of his fellow citizens. "He generally, indeed, neither intends to promote the public interest, nor knows how much he is promoting it. He intends only his own gain; and he is in this, as in many other things, led by an invisible hand to promote an end that was no part of his intention.

The world of the self-regulating market is one of remarkable moral simplicity, where people have no duty beyond self-interest and people enter into contracts, mutually beneficial, among equals. Of course, that was not the whole reality. Adam Smith somehow manages an extensive discussion of slavery (it is costly to maintain a slave, so it is profitable only for the best cash crops – tobacco, sugar, and, later, cotton), and yet its moral outrage never seems to seize him.

And then there is capital, *Das Kapital*, the sheer cumulative force of money. As Marx wrote a hundred and fifty years ago: "The very development of modern industry must progressively turn the scale in favor of the capitalist against the working man, and consequently the general tendency of capitalist production is not to raise, but to sink the average standard of wages or to push the value of labor more or less to its minimum limit."

If this was true in Marx's day, how much more is it in ours! Globalization puts workers hoping to earn a living wage in competition with desperately poor people in developing (and often authoritarian) countries. If that were not enough, automation threatens to eliminate most jobs altogether, even if the factory stays in the United States or Europe. The proletariat of the 19th and 20th centuries is the precariat of the 21st. A worker who loses one good job often has to take several bad ones. Those without a college education are especially vulnerable, though Ph.Ds. working low skill service sector jobs are common too. People who feel demoted and degraded are prey for reactionary, often racist politics.

But as the French economist Thomas Piketty points out, in periods of high inequality, income inequality is secondary. The really startling inequality is inequality of wealth. That is very much true today, and economic power lies less on the labor market than on the capital market. That is how a few hundred billionaires have more money than billions of people. Indeed the poor have no net wealth at all.

Moreover, money voraciously seeks higher return. More money changes currencies in the course of a single day than total global gross development product (GDP) over the course of a year. The average share of common stock is held not for years, not even for months, but for seconds, in lightning trades driven by computers. Normally things run smoothly, but when they don't there can be extreme volatility. An even more serious consideration is the time horizon which a speculative market imposes on corporate managers. A CEO who thinks about the long term will not survive to enjoy the long term. And since his (seldom her) "compensation package" (compensation for what hardship?) is in shares of company stock, s/he has an irresistible incentive to drive share price up as quickly as possible. The way to do that is to slash costs (fire workers) or just to cook the balance books (as Enron famously did). One of the most insidious concepts is Fiduciary Duty, whereby the managers of pension funds must seek maximum returns as ruthlessly as "Greed Is Good" Gordon Gecko.

Abuse invites reform, and innovative reform proposals abound. The explosion in wealth has not been accidental: it is the result of Republican cuts in capital gains and inheritance taxes, even on huge estates. Those cuts can be reversed, to the benefit of equity and government revenue for the common good.

No less significantly, the hyper-velocity of capital transfers invites a very small but enormously significant international transfer tax. Such a tax, without confiscating modest savings, could shave huge amounts of money off the destructive power of sheer speculation, favoring patient, longer-term investment by contrast. The money should go to build climate resilience in the least developed countries, those which have done the least to cause climate change but stand to suffer the most from it.

I once got an English paper back with my teacher's comment: "There may be no right answers in literature, but there certainly are some wrong ones." We may not know what we mean by equality, but we can all agree on the obscenity of inequality on the scale it exists today.

Yet it is too easy to rely on the glaringly bad as a substitute for the hard work of reaching shared ideals. What is equality? There is something oddly mathematical and neuter about the term. What is the relation to what we have learned about the extraordinarily gifted? The science writer Malcolm Gladwell recounts the discovery of the correlation of success getting on the Canadian hockey team and birth month. Those born in January had a few months' age advantage over the same birth year from October, and they were more apt to climb the ladder. This suggests that initial differences of no inherent significance could have enormous cumulative effect. The second finding comes from *Peak:* those who make extraordinary achievements are those who exceed a high threshold of sheer hours devoted to the effort. Past that point, a new realm of achievement becomes accessible. This suggests that the notion of innate genius is a romantic cliché. You do not have genius, but if you cultivate skill past a certain point, and you are receptive, then genius – spirit – may have you.

I mention excellence in a discussion of equality because justice should encourage the greatest diversity of human flourishing. It is no justification for aristocracy: anyone who has encountered would-be aristocrats has known more than their share of boors skilled only in toilet humor and bullying. But those willing to devote themselves to excellence with humility and a vision of helping others, deserve encouragement. It does not need to be a lot of money: who takes up the violin to get rich? Our era is gifted with a greater diversity of voices than any before us.

Meanwhile, there are the demands of empathy and the pang of acute suffering. We have wounded the planet in ways we can never heal, only salve. We live in the most catastrophic age of extinctions. Colonialism, slavery, and global capitalism have created injustices which reparations – however necessary – can never repair. We will have to live with acute awareness of the irreversible damage we have done.

Significantly, though, revolutionaries scorned appeals to conscience. They loathed depending upon the pity of the wealthy or the dream of new human beings. Marx and Lenin staked their campaigns upon sheer self-interest, not individual but collective; the interest of the industrial class.

Today we see a brisk revival of class struggle, articulated among others by *Jacobin Magazine* editor Bhaskar Sankara in his

Socialist Manifesto. Sankara insists that, as in Marx's time, socialist politics does not lie in the good intentions of idealists but in the raw power struggle of the working class – those, in other words, who lack capital and immediately depend on their labor for survival. Sankara argues that the decline of the industrial working class has been greatly exaggerated by those who wish to diminish its power. But he also enlarges his working class to include health care workers (not doctors) and teachers (not professors but school teachers and the underclass of non-tenured instructors).

Liberal Americans often look to an ideal of Scandinavian Social Democracy. Sankara is quick to disparage it. Norway affords its social programs thanks to oil. Social democracy runs off capitalism, and the more socially progressive it becomes, the more restive its capitalists grow. Ultimately they hold a capital strike: they threaten to withdraw their money and move it to a more docile country. For Sankara, this threat argues not for moderation but for attack: the state must appropriate the means of production and abolish private firms, at least in key economic sectors.

I think it would be facile to dismiss this manifesto based on the nightmares – as well as the sheer stultification – of 20th Century state socialism. But the fact remains that there are very few successes on record, and in some cases unions (that is, workers) played key roles in undoing state socialism – with national rivalry, religion, and the C.I.A. playing a supporting role (think of Poland).

A first step would be to socialize one sixth of the economy through Medicare for All and for the government to play a huge role in climate policy through the Green New Deal.

Meanwhile, there are vigorous efforts to reform capitalism. 2020 Presidential candidate Tom Steyer, who became a billionaire as a hedge fund manager investing in coal, is now trying to push major corporations to make a much faster climate transition. He and his colleagues argue that fossil fuel companies have "stranded assets." The oil and coal they have discovered but not extracted can never come out of the ground, because it cannot be burned without global catastrophe: it is therefore not only a risk to all of us; it is also a risk to the company's shareholders. Insofar as these companies' share price depends on fossil fuels, they are very dangerous investments. A few years ago, I argued with a seasoned investor in the Unitarian Universalist Association and my local church. He insisted that investing in clean energy was financially risky, and he kept the church's money in a famously smoky mutual fund. The current managers understand that if only for financial reasons, we are overdue a big shift.

The change here is that by arguing that a company has hinged its future on a socially intolerable risk, you succeed in worrying investors that their money depends on an activity that may not be allowed to proceed. That would endanger their profits. By raising this awareness, organizations like Trucost transform a social risk into a market risk, and suddenly the capitalist market begins more accurately to reflect ecological and social cost.

Will such capitalist reform make capitalism virtuous? It's unlikely, given the extreme gaps in wealth. Democratic socialists should persist.

But as I look at a world poised on the precipice on nuclear annihilation, nearing a point of no return on climate catastrophe, riven by gaps in wealth from unheard of riches to dire poverty even within rich countries, and to the point of homelessness, starvation, and climate as well as religious wars in poor countries, facing waves of forced migration, connected by pandemics and terrorism, I see no mechanism, but it capital or class or technology, that holds a formula for hope. I see only hope itself, unjustifiable but real, in the compassion of the human heart, the inventiveness of the human mind, and the resourcefulness of human society. This is where Creative Uncertainty will always part company with the ideologies of destiny.

In her wonderful book *A Paradise Built in Hell*, sociologist Rebecca Solnit discusses the extraordinary communities that arise in disaster. Starting with the San Francisco Fire of 1906, Solnit looks at the extreme cooperation of which people suddenly become capable. She compares such emergencies to festivals such as Mardi Gras, inversions of the quotidian social order that liberate enormous energy and creativity. Perhaps the Covid-19 pandemic, with its mandatory shutdown of "normal" life, has forced us into a liminal space, unable to continue with business as usual and aware of the possibilities of more radical change.

Alas, Paradise Now quickly becomes paradise yesterday, a community that dissolves into the cynicism of the so-called "real world." Does that change when the experiment, as it is now, is on the level of the world itself?

Not, I think, alone because of need. The challenge remains to channel the creativity of carnival into enduring institutions. But they must be institutions reinvented, with the fire of commitment that our times demand of us, with mutual and self-forgiveness that we need to work together, and with faith in the unconditional value of what we create. Unconditional hope alone offers ways out of danger, and unconditional hope alone affirms the life that makes all things new.

Bibliography

Listing the books that have inspired me is a humbling reminder how incompletely I have incorporated their fascinating findings. A new interdisciplinary global conversation is taking place, and I look forward to returning to it to study further and do it greater justice in future writings. Remembering how much Lewis Mumford's comprehensive bibliography helped my father and me, I have here listed more books than I have managed to quote.

Alberch, Per. *The Logic of Monsters: Evidence for Internal Constraint in Development and Evolution.* 1989. https://doi.org/10.1016/S0016-6995(89)80006-3.

Arendt, Hannah. *The Human Condition.* Chicago: University of Chicago Press, 1958; 2nd Edition 2013.

Bakewell, Sarah. *How to Live: A Life of Montaigne.* Other Press, 2010.

Bate, Jonathan. *Soul of the Age: A Biography of the Mind of William Shakespeare.* Random House, 2009.

Bateson, Gregory. *Steps to an Ecology of Mind.* Chandler, 1972.

Bateson, Gregory. *Mind and Nature: A Necessary Unity.* Dutton, 1979.

Bateson, Gregory, and Bateson, Mary Catherine. *Angels Fear: Toward an Epistemology of the Sacred.* Macmillan, 1987.

Beiser, Frederick. *After Hegel: German Philosophy 1840-1900.* Princeton University Press, 2014.

Bentley, Joseph, and Toth, Michael. *Exploring Wicked Problems.* Archway Publishing, 2020.

Benyus, Janine. *Biomimicry: Innovation Inspired by Nature.* Harper, 1998.

Bertalanffy, Ludwig von. *General System Theory.* Braziller, 1968; 2nd Edition,2003.

Bergson, Henri. Bergson: Key Writings, edited by Keith Ansell Pearson and John Mullarkey, London: Continuum, 2002.

Bergson, Henri. Creative Evolution, tr., Arthur Mitchell, New York: Dover, 1998 [1911].

Blumberg, Mark. *Freaks of Nature: What Anomalies Tell Us About Development and Evolution*. Oxford University Press, 2008.

Boehm, Christopher, *Moral Origins: The Evolution of Virtue, Altruism, and Shame*. Basic Books, 2012.

Bollier, David. *Think Like a Commoner: A Short Introduction to the Life of the Commons*. New Society Publishers, 2014.

Braver, Lee. *Heidegger: Thinking of Being (Key Contemporary Thinkers)*. Polity, 2014.

Capra, Fritjof. *The Web of Life: A New Scientific Understanding of Living Systems*. Anchor, 1997.

Carr, Nicholas. *The Glass Cage: How Our Computers Are Changing Us*. Norton, 2014.

Cline, Eric H. *1177 B.C.: The Year Civilization Collapsed*. Princeton University Press, 2015.

Cohen, Stephen. *Soviet Fates and Lost Alternatives*. Columbia University Press, 2009.

Critchley, Simon. *Tragedy, the Greeks, and Us*. Vintage, 2019.

Daly, Herman E. and Cobb, John B. *For the Common Good: Redirecting the Economy Toward Community, the Environment, and a Sustainable Future*. Beacon Press, 1989.

Darwell, Stephen. *Honor, History, and Relationship: Essays in Second Person Ethics*. Oxford University Press, 2015.

Davis, David Brion. *Inhuman Bondage: The Rise and Fall of Slavery in the New World*. Oxford University Press, 2008.

Deacon, Terrence W. *Incomplete Nature: How Mind Emerged from Matter*. W. W. Norton, 2011.

Deresiewicz, William. *Excellent Sheep: The Miseducation of the American Elite.* Free Press, 2014.

Dewey, John. *Collected Works*. Pergamon Media, 2015.

Diamond, Jared. *Collapse: How Societies Choose to Fail or Succeed.* Penguin, 2013.

Eisenberg, Evan. *The Ecology of Eden: An Inquiry into the Dream of Paradise and a New Vision of Our Role in Nature.* Vintage, 1999.

Eisler, Riane. *The Chalice and the Blade*. Harper, 2011.

Ellsberg, Daniel. *The Doomsday Machine: Confessions of a Nuclear War Planner. Bloomsbury USA; 1st edition, 2017.*

Figal, Günter. *Martin Heidegger zur Einführung.* ◎ Junius Verlag; 7th edition, 2018.

Frischoff, Baruch and Kadvany, John. *Risk: A Very Short Introduction.* Oxford UniversityPress, 2014.

Fry, Douglas P. *Beyond War: The Human Potential for Peace*. Oxford University Press, 2007.

Gladwell, Malcolm, *Outliers: The Story of Success.* Little, Brown, and Co. 2008.

Godfrey-Smith, Peter. *Metazoa: Animal Life and the Birth of the Mind.* Farrar, Straus, and Giroux, 2020.

Gombrich, E. H. *Art and Illusion.* Princeton, reprint edition 2000.

Gould, Stephen J. *The Structure of Evolutionary Theory*. Harvard University Press, 2002.

Grant, Adam. *Think Again: The Power of Knowing What You Don't Know*. Viking, 2021.

Greenblatt, Stephen, *The Swerve: How the World Became Modern.* Norton, 2011.

Grossman, David. *On Killing: The Psychological Cost of Learning to Kill in War and Society*. Open Road Media, 2014.

Hamilton, Clive, *Earthmasters: The Dawn of the Age of Climate Engineering*. Yale, 2015.

Hecht, Jennifer Michael. *Doubt: A History: The Great Doubters and Their Legacy of Innovation from Socrates and Jesus to Thomas Jefferson and Emily Dickinson*. Harper, 2010.

Heffernan, Margaret. *Uncharted: How to Navigate the Future*. Simon and Schuster, 2020.

Henderson, Rebecca. *Reimagining Capitalism in a World on Fire.* Public Affairs, 2020.

Isaacson, Walter, *Leonardo da Vinci.* Simon and Schuster, 2017.

Jablonka, Eva and Lamb, Marion. *Evolution in Four Dimensions.* M.I.T., 2006.

Johnson, Curtis, *Darwin's Dice: The Idea of Chance in the Work of Charles Darwin.* Oxford University Press, 2015.

Kaplan, Fred M. *The Bomb: Presidents, Generals, and the Secret History of Nuclear War.* Simon and Schuster, 2020.

Kenny, Anthony. *A New History of Western Philosophy.* Oxford University Press, 2015.

Kinderman, William. *Beethoven.* Oxford University Press, 2009.

Koestler, Arthur. *The Ghost in the Machine*. London: Hutchinson, 1967.

Koestler, Arthur. *The Act of Creation*. London: Hutchinson, 1976.

Kolbert, Elizabeth. *The Sixth Extinction*. Henry Holt, 2014.

Kolbert, Elizabeth. *Under a White Sky: The Nature of the Future.* Crown, 2021.

Krimsky, Sheldon, and Gruber, Jeremy. *Genetic Explanations: Sense and Nonsense.* Harvard University Press, 2013.

Kuhn, Thomas S. and Hacking, Ian. *The Structure of Scientific Revolutions.* University of Chicago Press, 2014.

Leland, Kevin N. *Darwin's Unfinished Symphony: How Culture Made the Human Mind.* Princeton, 2018.

Lewis-Williams, David. *Mind in the Cave: Consciousness and the Origins of Art.* Thames and Hudson, 2004.

Lindley, David. *Uncertainty: Einstein, Heisenberg, Bohr, and the Struggle for the Soul of Science.* Anchor Books, 2008.

McTighe, Jay and Wiggins, Grant. *Essential Questions: Opening Doors to Student Understanding.* A.S.C.D., 2013.

Mann, Charles. *1491: New Revelations of the Americas Before Columbus.* Vintage, 2006.

Mann, Michael. *The Sources of Social Power: A History of Power from the Beginning to A.D. 1760.* Cambridge, 1987.

Massey, Heath. *The Origin of Time: Heidegger and Bergson* (SUNY series in Contemporary Continental Philosophy). SUNY Press, 2015.

Mayor, Adrienne. *Gods and Robots: Myths, Machines, and Ancient Dreams of Technology.* Princeton University Press, 2018.

Meadows, Donella H. *Thinking in Systems.* Chelsea Green Publishing, 2007.

Merchant, Carolyn. *The Death of Nature: Women, Ecology, and the Scientific Revolution.* Harper and Row, 1980.

Midgley, Mary. *Evolution as Religion.* Taylor and Francis, 1985.

Milo, Daniel S. *Good Enough: The Tolerance for Mediocrity in Nature and Society*. Harvard University Press, 2019.

Mindell, David. *Our Robots, Ourselves: Robotics and Myths of Autonomy*. Viking, 2015.

Mishra, Pankaj. *The Age of Anger*. Juggernaut Books, 2020.

Monbiot, George. *The Age of Consent: A Manifesto for a New World Order*. Flamingo, 2010.

Mumford, Lewis. *The Myth of the Machine,* Volume One: *Technics and Human Development*. Harcourt, Brace, 1967.

Mumford, Lewis, *The Myth of the Machine,* Volume Two: *The Pentagon of Power.* Harcourt, 1974.

Murphy, Cullen. *God's Jury: The Inquisition and the Making of the Modern World*. New York: Mariner Books, 2012.

Nagel, Thomas. *Mind and Cosmos: Why the Materialist Neo-Darwinian Conception of Nature Is Almost Certainly False*. Oxford University Press, 2012.

Noble, Denis. *The Music of Life: Biology Beyond the Genome*. Oxford University Press, 2008.

Noble, Denis. *Dance to the Tune of Life: Biological Relativity*. Cambridge, 2016.

Northrop, F. S. C. *The Meeting of East and West.* Macmillan, 1946.

Oreskes, Naomi and Conway, Eric. *The Collapse of Western Civilization: A View from the Future*. Columbia University Press, 2015.

Passet, Rene. *L'économique et le vivant*. Economica, 1996.

Perrow, Charles. *Normal Accidents: Living with High-Risk Technologies.* Princeton University Press, 2011.

Piketty, Thomas. *Capital in the 21st Century*. Harvard University Press, 2014.

Piketty, Thomas. *Capital and Ideology*. Harvard University Press, 2020.

Pocock, J. G. A. *Politics, Language, and Time*. University of Chicago Press, 1960 (Athaneum), 1989.

Precht, Richard David. *Erkenne die Welt: eine Geschichte der Philosophie. Antike und Mittelalter*. Goldmann, 2015.

Precht, Richard David. *Erkenne dich selbst: eine Gischichte der Philolsophie*, II. Goldmann, 2017.

Prigogine, Ilya and Stengers, Isabelle. *Order Out of Chaos*. Bantam Books, 1984.

Prigogine, Ilya. *The End of Certainty*. Free Press/ Macmillan, 1997.

Raworth, Kate. *Doughnut Economics: How to Think Like a 21st Century Economist*. Chelsea Green Publishing, 2017.

Redecker, Eva von. *Revolution für das Leben: Philosophie der neuen Protestformen*. Fischer, 2020.

Reiss, John O. *Not By Design: Retiring Darwin's Watchmaker*. University of California Press, 2009.

Riskin, Jessica. *The Restless Clock: A History of the Centuries-Long Argument over What Makes Living Things Tick*. University of Chicago Press, 2016.

Saramago, Jose. *Blindness*. Mariner Books, 1999/2013.

Scharf, Caleb. *The Copernicus Complex: Our Cosmic Significance in a Universe of Planets and Possibilities*. Farrar, Straus, and Giroux, 2014.

Schell, Jonathan. *The Fate of the Earth*. Knopf, 1982.

Schulz, Kathryn. *Being Wrong: Adventures in the Margin of Error*. Harper Collins, 2013.

Scott, Robert H. and Moss, Gregory. *The Significance of Indeterminacy: Perspectives from Asian and Continental Philosophy.* Routledge, 2018.

Shapin, Steven. *The Scientific Revolution.* University of Chicago Press, 2018.

Sherman, Jeremy. *Neither Ghost Nor Machine: The Emergence and Nature of Selves.* Columbia University Press, 2018.

Smolin, Lee. *Time Reborn: From the Crisis in Physics to the Future of the Universe.* Mariner Books, 2013.

Solnit, Rebecca. *A Paradise Built in Hell: The Extraordinary Communities That Arise in Disaster.* Penguin Books, 2010.

Stott, Rebecca. *Darwin's Ghosts: The Secret History of Evolution.* Random House, 2012.

Strevens, Michael. *The Knowledge Machine: How Irrationality Created Modern Science.* Liveright, 2020.

Sucher, Sandra J. *The Moral Leader*. Routledge, 2007.

Sunkara, Bhaskar. *The Socialist Manifesto: The Case for Radical Politics in an Era of Extreme Inequality.* Basic Books, 2019.

Tomasello, Michael. *A Natural History of Human Morality*. Harvard University Press, 2016.

Toulmin, Stephen. *Cosmopolis: The Hidden Agenda of Modernity.* University of Chicago Press, 1990.

Tse, Peter Ulrich. *The Neural Basis of Free Will: Criterial Causation.* M.I.T. Press, 2013.

Turkle, Sherry. *Alone Together: Why We Expect More from Technology and Less from Each Other.* Basic Books, 2011.

Unger, Roberto Mangabeira and Smolin, Lee. *The Singular Universe and the Reality of Time.* Cambridge University Press, 2014.

Unger, Roberto Mangabeira. *The Knowledge Economy.* Penguin, 2019.

Wagner, Andreas. *The Arrival of the Fittest.* Current Publishing, 2014.

Whitehead, Alfred North. *Process and Reality: An Essay in Cosmology.* Corrected Edition: Free Press, 1979.

Williams, Raymond. *Keywords: A Vocabulary of Culture and Society.* Oxford University Press, 1985.

Wulf, Andrea. *The Invention of Nature: Alexander Von Humboldt's New World.* Vintage, 2015.

Zolli, Andrew and Healy, Ann Marie. *Resilience: Why Things Bounce Back.* Free Press, 2012.

Made in the USA
Monee, IL
14 October 2021